A SHORT HISTORY OF WOOL
AND ITS MANUFACTURE

A SHORT HISTORY

OF WOOL

AND

ITS MANUFACTURE

(MAINLY IN ENGLAND)

BY

E. LIPSON

'I thanke God, and ever shall,
It is the Sheepe hath payed for all.'

WILLIAM HEINEMANN LTD
MELBOURNE   LONDON   TORONTO

First published 1953

MADE AND PRINTED IN GREAT BRITAIN
BY W. S. COWELL LTD, BUTTER MARKET, IPSWICH

ONULP

Contents

PART I
WOOL AND SHEEP

CHAPTER   PAGE

I   INTRODUCTION   I

II   ENGLISH WOOL   10

III MERINO AND CROSSBRED WOOL   36

PART II
WOOL MANUFACTURES

IV   EARLY HISTORY   49

V   ORGANIZATION   63

VI   STATE CONTROL   97

VII   PROCESSES AND INVENTIONS   118

VIII THE NINETEENTH AND TWENTIETH CENTURIES   152

      Appendix—GEOGRAPHICAL DISTRIBUTION   179

      BIBLIOGRAPHICAL NOTE   193

      INDEX   195

Preface

Part II incorporates material drawn from my *History of the Woollen and Worsted Industries* (first published in 1921), together with numerous changes and additions.

January 1953

E. LIPSON

PART I

WOOL AND SHEEP

CHAPTER ONE

Introduction

AMONG THE TEXTILE fibres which have been utilized through
the ages to clothe man's body, wool—the coat of the sheep—
occupies a unique position. It is not alone the oldest but also
one which has been continuously and universally used. In the
Biblical story of the Creation the keeper of sheep shares with
the grower of corn the task of satisfying the most primitive
and enduring of human needs; and from the infancy of the
race down to the advanced civilization of our own day wool
has retained the peculiar qualities which account for its
primacy over other textile raw materials in temperate lands.
It is spun into thread with ease, it is light and durable, its
serrations (scales) and elasticity enable cloth to be made which
absorbs moisture and preserves heat. It is used for numerous
purposes—for apparel (garments woven and knitted) as well
as for furnishing fabrics of all kinds including floor coverings
(carpets and rugs), curtains, blankets and tapestries. The part
which wool has played in the national economy of England
entitles it to be considered one of the pillars of the state: its
importance in world economy is reflected in the status which
it has enjoyed from early times as one of the major commodities
of international trade. A report of the United States tariff
commission in 1921 pointed out that the subject of wool has
'a great many ramifications. It touches international policy in
regard to the control of raw materials. It involves domestic
policy with respect to the use of our natural resources, to
the relations between producers, middlemen and consumers,
and to the development of co-operative methods. It is related
to many agricultural questions—use of the soil, management
of livestock, choice of crops. It also has a vital relation to the
consumers' interests.'

An outstanding feature of wool is its immense variety of
types: indeed it is computed that they comprise several

thousands. During the first world war under the British government's purchase scheme wool experts classified Australian wool into approximately 850 types; during the second world war the list was increased to 1500 (and 950 types of New Zealand wool). In the United States the standard samples kept at the customs-houses for testing the qualities of imported wool amounted to 381. In practice a much smaller quantity of grades, well under a hundred, suffices for normal trade requirements. The variations in the character of wool are due to different causes. One is the breed of sheep: the number of breeds runs into three figures. A common classification of these breeds comprises merino, crossbred, English long wool, and 'native' unimproved.[1] Other factors are climate, pasturage and skilful farming (for instance, care in the selection of breed.[2]) The chief qualities of wool are fine, medium, and coarse: the first two (reckoned to be four-fifths of the annual world output) are used for wearing apparel and the coarse (one-fifth) for carpets and rugs. The finest wool is produced by merino breeds; the medium wool by crossbreds of which the fleece holds a middle place between the finer merinos and the coarser English long wool; and the carpet wool by 'native' unimproved breeds. Within these main divisions there is an infinite range of 'sorts;' even individual sheep may yield several 'sorts' in the same fleece. The classification of these wool types is based primarily on fineness and length of fibre as well as on soundness, handle, elasticity, clean condition, colour, felting properties.[3]

The vast diversity in grades of wool provides opportunity for the exercise of skill in blending the different fibres, and gives scope for the creative powers of the craftsman even in the

[1] Historically crossbreds are crosses between merino and English breeds. But the term is also applied to what have now become pure breeds in their own right. They are less than 60's (see note 3).

[2] The price of over 4,000 guineas has been paid at a Sydney auction for a ram; rams have been sold privately for 5,000 guineas each.

[3] *Fineness* applies essentially to the spinning quality of the wool. It is designated by the 'count' of the yarn, *i.e.* the number of hanks to which one pound of wool can be spun. A hank of worsted yarn is 560 yards long; a hank (or skein) of woollen yarn is 256 yards long. If 10 hanks of worsted yarn weigh one pound, then the wool is classified as number 10 (or 10's) or 10 count; and accordingly the numerical term 10's denotes that the length of a pound of worsted yarn is 5,600 yards. The finer the wool, the higher is the count or spinning capacity: thus the quality of merino wool is 60's and upwards. In contrast with the English system of numerical

initial stages of manufacture. On the other hand the standardization of the wool textile industry is not practicable to the
same degree as in other textile industries. Moreover it is
officially stated that 'the large number of grades complicates
the marketing of the raw wool and has prevented the adoption
of the techniques developed for stabilizing prices in other industries using primary commodities.' In the absence of suitable
standards it becomes difficult to organize a futures market; and
while the latter existed in Antwerp and still exists in New York,
it has been 'little used by the British wool textile industry.' The
significance of a wide range of fluctuating prices may be gauged
from the fact that normally clean virgin wool accounted for
about one-third of the total cost of cloth.[1]

Estimates of the world's sheep population and wool production are unreliable; furthermore a large proportion of sheep
yield either no wool or inferior wool unsuited for apparel
fabrics. However these estimates afford a general idea of the
statistical trend: in normal years the world's number of sheep
is placed at over 750 millions,[2] and the world's output of wool
at about 4,000 million pounds annually.[3] Of these totals the
British Commonwealth claims the lion's share, for it possesses
approximately one-third of the sheep, grows nearly one-half of
the wool, and furnishes the bulk of the exportable surplus.
Within the past hundred years the northern hemisphere has
been displaced by the southern as the leading source of wool
supply, though the former remains the leading consumer.
Sheep are raised in every quarter of the globe—especially

terms, the American system is a blood classification (*e.g.* half-blood, quarter-blood,
etc.). The latter now signifies not the proportion of merino blood but the quality
of wool formerly found in sheep of one-half (or one-quarter, etc.) merino blood.
The *length* of staple (fibre) varies greatly. It may range up to 5 inches (merino and
crossbred) and up to 15 inches or more (long wool). *Soundness* (strength) denotes
ability to stand the strain of manufacture. *Handle* denotes softness of feel. *Elasticity*
denotes ability to return to normal length after stretching. *Clean condition* denotes
freedom from impurities.
[1] Raw wool was estimated to account for 10–15 per cent. of the total cost of a
wool suit or overcoat. The phenomenal rise in the price of wool after the second
world war affected these proportions.
[2] 1939—752 m.; 1950—715 m.
[3] 1939—3,940 m. lb.; 1950—3,835 m. lb. On a clean basis (see p. 6) the world's
annual wool clip is estimated at about 2,000 m. lb.

Australia, New Zealand, Union of South Africa, Argentina, Uruguay, Russia, India, Turkey, Spain, China, United States and Great Britain—the first five are the chief exporting countries,[1] while the last two alone figure in the front rank as both producers and manufacturers of wool. Hence there is a marked contrast between the restricted area of cotton-growing and the almost illimitable field of wool-growing. Nevertheless wool production has only expanded by one-third in the past half century, although the standard of living and the world's population have considerably advanced. In nearly all countries the indications are that the number of sheep has passed its meridian. Indeed the deficiency in the output of wool would have been much more conspicuous but for a notable increase in the weight of the fleece due to improved breeding.[2] To meet the shortage woollen manufacturers have recourse to other fibres— animal, vegetable and synthetic—which are blended with wool. These substitutes are mohair (hair of Angora goat bred in Turkey, United States and Union of South Africa), alpaca (hair of alpaca found in Peru and Bolivia), cashmere (hair of cashmere goat in Kashmir, Tibet and China), camel, silk, cotton, rayon; in addition re-worked wool[3] is used in substantial quantities. The trend away from fabrics of pure virgin wool was accelerated by the desire to produce cheaper wearing apparel.

One important factor which has served to limit the growth— and even to diminish the numbers—of the sheep population is the curtailment of the area available for raising sheep. We can trace several stages in the evolution of sheep husbandry. In the pioneer stage, or open range system, the flocks were free to roam over unfenced and unoccupied land which was public domain—wide stretches of territory utilized only for pastoral purposes. The drawback here was that it led to congestion: too

[1] In 1948 they accounted for 60% of world output and 94% of world exports. The percentage naturally varies, e.g. it was 85% of world exports in 1950. The United States, the United Kingdom and the Continent of Europe imported 95% of world imports in 1950.

[2] In New South Wales the weight of the fleece doubled 1876–1935. The total Australian clip was nearly doubled 1891–1926 although the number of sheep was stationary.

[3] Shoddy and mungo.

many sheep were grazed and over-stocking caused serious deterioration of the pastures. In the second stage large private estates (ranches), carved out of the public land, were bought or leased from the state by the flockmasters, who were thereby enabled to adopt scientific methods of breeding and to exercise skill in the art of flock management. Ranches are to be found in Australia, South America and in the west of the United States. In Australia and New Zealand the great sheep runs or 'stations' are divided into several paddocks, which preserve natural conditions but within fences; and the sheep can be moved from one to another. The practice saves labour because fewer shepherds are needed if sheep lands are fenced; it increases the weight and improves the quality of the sheep; and it is more productive of lambs.

The third stage emerges when the pressure of population necessitates the most economical use of the resources of the land, and the soil is exploited primarily to raise crops. The result is a further contraction of the open range system,[1] since the public domain is closely settled with 'homesteaders' who devote themselves to intensive cultivation. Similarly in course of time vast estates tend to be broken up into small farms, either compulsorily to satisfy the hunger for land or voluntarily owing to taxation. Once this stage arrives sheep husbandry is no longer pursued for its own sake; it becomes part and parcel of a mixed farming economy in which the raising of crops takes precedence over the raising of sheep. The transition from public ranges (in the United States) and private ranches (in Australia and South America) to the small farms characteristic of Europe has already made considerable headway under the spur of agricultural settlement and immigration. The consequences are reflected in the diminished size of the flocks which were formerly of great magnitude. Thus a generation ago Australia had eighteen flocks exceeding 100,000 sheep apiece, and flocks of 10,000 and over accounted for half the total number. The fact that the tendency has set in towards relatively small flocks raised at a higher cost must heighten the price of wool, while the pre-occupation of the farmer with

---

[1] The creation of national forests, however, provides opportunities for grazing.

crops and meat is likely to affect adversely the preparation of the wool for the market. The reservoirs of wool cheaply produced and carefully prepared are shrinking, and the search for substitutes will be accelerated.

We must now turn from the production of wool to marketing. Wool is sold mainly in the form of fleece wool.[1] The first and finest clip is termed lamb's or hog's wool and subsequent clips are known as fleece wool. In its natural condition, when it is sheared either by hand or machines, the fleece is grease wool; after the elimination of impurities (animal grease, soil and other extraneous matter) it is scoured or clean wool. If sheep are washed previous to shearing, a part of the foreign substances embedded in the fleece will be extracted; but manufacturers are said to prefer to buy wool 'in the grease' because the latter hinders the wool from felting. Machinery is now used for scouring wool, and the decrease in weight thereby effected is called shrinkage. The extent of shrinkage which wool undergoes in the process of cleansing varies enormously according to the type of wool. The loss of weight may be as low as one-third (or less) or as high as two-thirds (or more)—that is, a hundred pounds of raw wool may yield under thirty pounds of clean wool. The shrinkage is much higher in merino wool[2] than in English long wool. The rapid expansion of the market in the nineteenth century was the principal factor in inducing the breeders to offer their wool for sale in a form acceptable to the buyers. Australia was the pioneer in improving marketing methods. Every whole fleece—before it leaves the shearing shed at the sheep 'station'—is first skirted by removing the inferior parts around the edges; next it is classed (graded) mainly on the basis of fineness and length of staple; and then it is packed in the bale assigned to its class. Subsequently, frequently at the mill but sometimes by the wool merchant, the individual fleece is sorted (divided) into a variety of qualities or 'sorts' which may

[1] Fleece wool is clipped from the sheep. Skin wool is removed from the skin of slaughtered animals.
[2] A writer in 1719 stated that the waste in Spanish wool *en suin*, when it was well washed, was commonly 53 per cent.

exceed a dozen in number.[1] In the eighteenth century Dyer in his poem *The Fleece* (1757) wrote:

> In the same fleece diversity of wool
> Grows intermingled, and excites the care
> Of curious skill to sort the sev'ral kinds.

'Sell and repent but sell.' The growers' slogan was born of the experience of wide fluctuations in the prices of wool. From year to year prices may vary considerably.[2] The reason for this instability is that in the farming industry (unlike the manufacturing industries) supply cannot be readily adjusted to demand; the number of sheep cannot be rapidly augmented or diminished; and so the wool clip may not reflect the actual requirements at the moment of the consuming countries. For the disposal of the clip the grower has the choice of several channels of marketing. He can sell to speculative buyers or to mill agents; he can utilize the services of brokers; he can place it in the hands of a co-operative association. Private sales are the oldest method: the wool merchant, formerly known as the wool stapler, was the pivot of the commercial organization of the wool trade in England for many hundreds of years. In some countries this method still prevails, notably in the United States where wool is mostly sold by private treaty either by the

---

[1] Luccock, a wool stapler, in his book on *Wool* (1805) affirmed that wool in England was sometimes broken up into seventeen 'sorts' and in Spain into three 'sorts.'

[2] Taking 1914 as 100 the wholesale price index (United Kingdom Board of Trade) of wool between the two world wars was 198 (1924), 116 (1929), 56 (1932), 113 (1937), 80 (1938). The spectacular rise in prices after the second world war was one of the astonishing phenomena of the post-war epoch. Civilian demands stimulated by a better distribution of incomes and by the need to replenish depleted wardrobes, combined with stock-piling for military purposes, increased wool consumption several hundred million pounds above the pre-war level. Production lagged behind; and the new level of consumption was only made possible because stocks of raw wool had been accumulated during the war. These stocks, known as Joint-Organization stocks, amounted at the end of the war to $10\frac{1}{2}$ million bales (a bale is approximately 300 lb.); and they were marketed in five years (1946–51) alongside of the current clip. The trend of prices, when free auctions were resumed in 1946 after war-time control lapsed, was as follows. Taking the pre-war years 1934–8 as 100, the wholesale price index of wool was 170 (1946), 200 (1947), 261 (1948), 320 (1949), 671 (1950). Then—with the exhaustion of the surplus stocks and a wave of panic buying—wool prices soared to dizzy heights, reaching their peak in March 1951 when the index figure was 1,476. (To take a specific instance: in September 1946 merino 64's were 42d. per lb. and in March 1951 they fetched 314d. per lb.) Then came a sudden turn of the wheel: in July 1951 the index figure fell to 716, *i.e.* less than one-half of the March level.

individual producer or through co-operative associations of growers. Similarly South America adheres to the practice of private sales. The alternative system of open competitive bidding at public auctions is the distinctive feature of the wool market in the British Commonwealth—England, Australia, New Zealand and South Africa. The clips are offered for sale on the producers' behalf by brokerage houses and co-operative associations. The advantages claimed for auction sales are firstly that they afford purchasers a wider choice of clips; secondly a competitive spirit is induced in the growers to produce wool which in quality, grading and appearance will bring them credit; thirdly higher prices are ensured by the presence of many buyers, and a glut can be avoided or mitigated by arrangements between the associations of producers and brokers limiting the amount put on the market in any month. The drawback is that the selling brokers, who handle the wool on a commission basis, acquire a measure of control over the pastoral industry since they are accustomed to finance the wool grower; they advance loans on the security of the clip and supply the 'sheep stations' with their varied requirements.

The holding of public auctions originated in the early nineteenth century in London, where they continue to be held to this day. Here is a description of a London auction in 1911. 'The sale takes place in one large room in the wool exchange on Coleman Street. Selling begins at 4 o'clock. The room is constructed similar to an amphitheatre. The moment the first lot is called out [the densely packed audience] burst forth in one wild chorus of yells and howls. The next number [is sounded] and immediately a dozen or more excited bidders leap to their feet and so on. Excitement on the Stock Exchange is tame compared with it. An Australian said: "We call our wool sales in Sydney the dog fight, but this is the world's menagerie turned loose." ' While London retains its status as a leading world market for wool—as might be expected in a country whose consumption of this raw material has approached a thousand million pounds—yet the bulk of the Australian clip is no longer shipped to England for sale at public auctions.

Instead the auction sales are held in Australia and are frequented by buyers from many countries. The change over began a century ago; and London was gradually superseded as the principal market for the disposal of the wool raised in the Empire because the oversea growers were spared the charges paid as freight, insurance, storage and dock dues; moreover, when the clip was shipped to London, several months elapsed before the growers received full payment.

The disposal of the home clip raised in England formerly reflected, as might be expected, a variety of practices. Some producers sold direct to merchants as they had done for hundreds of years. Some sold direct to manufacturers—this was less frequent since manufacturers generally preferred to rely on middlemen who could provide the 'sorts' or qualities specifically required by the mills, although the best spinners bought and sorted their own wool in order to avoid the mixing in of inferior grades. And lastly some employed brokers who might sell the clip privately to merchants and manufacturers or offer it by auction. The bulk of the wool was apparently sold at country fairs either privately or more commonly by auction.

In consequence of recent changes in the system of marketing, all British wool is now sold under the National Farmers' Union Wool Marketing Scheme.[1] Sheep farmers register with the government and undertake to accept a fixed price for their wool, which is then sold by auction. When auction prices considerably exceed the fixed annual price, provision is made for returning the excess profits to the farmers.

[1] The British Wool Marketing Board is responsible for marketing Britain's homegrown wool.

CHAPTER TWO

English Wool

FOR MANY CENTURIES Englishmen cherished the conviction that English wool was the best in the world. The tradition went back to early times when the wool produced in this country enjoyed immense repute. Thus Dionysius Periegetes, a geographer of antiquity, stated that the fleece of the sheep was 'so soft and fine' that it was spun until it was 'comparable to a spider's web.' More than a thousand years later the Elizabethan antiquary, Lambard, affirmed that 'the exceeding fineness of the fleece passeth all other in Europe at this day.' And Dryden wrote:

> Though Jason's Fleece was fam'd of old,
> The British wool is growing gold;
> No mines can more of wealth supply.
> It keeps the peasant from the cold,
> And takes for kings the Tyrian dye.

The esteem in which it was held is enshrined in the Woolsack, 'the seat of our wise learned judges,' for in the national economy wool boasted pride of place. It was our chief raw material, the indispensable basis of our greatest industry, and the most highly prized of our products in other countries. Every class in the community, whether landlord, farmer, manufacturer or artisan, had an interest in wool; and it provided a fertile field for economic controversy.

The history of wool production in England throughout the greater part of the middle ages is a story of ordered growth, in which there was no marked encroachment of pasture-farming upon corn-growing. Down to the fifteenth century the traditional balance between the two branches of husbandry remained unimpaired. The sheep farmer kept to remote regions or to the waste that was no man's property. The Cistercians, who were

pre-eminent among the pioneers of wool-growing—at the time
of Richard I's captivity they devoted a year's wool to his
ransom—established themselves in secluded and sparsely-
inhabited districts. Then as the middle ages drew to a close,
under the impact of an increasing demand for raw material,
the sheep industry expanded rapidly and was directly responsible for an agrarian revolution—the substitution of wool-
growing for corn-growing.

Many factors combined to bring about this momentous
development. The pursuit of tillage was not always an attractive
proposition, because the export of corn was forbidden when
prices were high and the cost of agricultural labour had risen
considerably. While tillage was thus heavily handicapped,
English wool readily found a market at home and abroad.
Formerly the bulk of the wool grown in England was exported
as raw material 'unto a more ingenious nation' to be worked
up by the famous looms of Bruges, Ypres and Ghent. But after
the middle of the fourteenth century the native cloth manufacture made great strides and created a corresponding demand
for wool on the part of the English clothiers—for the first condition of a flourishing industry is an ample supply of raw material.
The profit derived by graziers from the growing of wool
tempted landlords and farmers to convert arable land into
pasture, and sheep were regarded 'as the most profitablest
cattle that any man can have.' 'The foot of the sheep,' men
said, 'turns sand into gold.' Hence strong inducements existed
in favour of sheep-farming; its profits were higher and its
expenses in labour costs were lower than those of tillage. There
was more profit, said a contemporary writer, 'by grazing of ten
acres to the occupier alone than is in tillage of twenty;' and it
was natural that the farmer had no 'joy to set his plough in the
ground.' Sometimes indeed the woollen manufacturer himself
became a sheep farmer. One famous clothier of the fifteenth
century, John Tame, kept large flocks of sheep at Fairford and
the wool produced there was worked up in his weaving sheds at
Cirencester. In fact the rise of the textile industries, while it
contributed to the depopulation of the countryside whenever
grassland superseded cornfields, served to provide some openings

for those cut adrift from the soil. In any case the agrarian changes afford striking proof of the progress of the cloth trade, and reveal its influence in diverting the energies of the rural community into channels which might best satisfy the needs and requirements of the textile industries.

The growth of sheep-farming in England was a continuous movement from the late fifteenth to the late eighteenth century, but its pinnacle was reached under the Early Tudors. It was the most important event in the social history of the sixteenth century and filled the minds of statesmen, preachers and writers to an extent which only finds an adequate parallel in the religious changes contemporaneous with it. It was the theme of countless sermons, pamphlets, ballads and acts of parliament, and awakened a storm that swept over the land like a hurricane.[1] The immense quantity of sheep called forth on every side indignant protests. 'God gave the earth to men to inhabit,' said Tyndale, 'and not unto sheep.' A poet, Bastard, wrote:

> Sheep have eaten up our meadows and our downs,
> Our corn, our wood, whole villages and towns.

It attracted the marked attention of foreigners. 'They have,' observed a Venetian (c. 1500), 'an enormous number of sheep.' Polydore Vergil in a description of England went so far as to assert that 'of Englishmen more are graziers and masters of cattle than husbandmen or labourers in tilling of the field.' It was suggested that 'for the abundant store of flocks so increasing everywhere the whole realm might rightly be called Sheppey.' Even the towns had commons on which were pastured sheep belonging to the inhabitants, and the herdsman was a municipal officer. The development of pasturage at the expense of tillage aroused the more concern because it involved depopulation of villages. 'Where,' cried Latimer in a sermon preached before Edward VI, 'have been a great many householders and inhabitants, there is now but a shepherd and his dog.' Sir

---

[1] While contemporary descriptions could be applied to particular localities, the statistical evidence conveys a different impression of the extent to which the kingdom as a whole was affected.

Thomas More, in a famous passage in *Utopia*, denounced sheep as 'devourers of men.' 'They unpeople towns and villages, turning the best inhabited places into solitudes; tenants are turned out of their possessions and either beg or rob. One shepherd can look after a flock which will stock an extent of ground that would require many hands if it were to be ploughed and reaped.' A ballad of the time ran:

> The towns go down, the land decays;
> Great men maketh nowadays
>   a sheep-cote in the church;
> Commons to close and keep;
> Poor folk for bread cry and weep;
> Towns pulled down to pasture sheep;
>   this is the new guise!

The social unrest evoked by the spread of sheep-farming with its attendant consequences—the eviction of the peasantry from their ancestral holdings, the curtailment of agricultural employment and the usurpation of the village commons—found vent in riots and insurrections in an age that did not easily brook invasion of its traditional way of life whether religious or economic. No government could view with indifference the disintegrating forces which menaced a seemingly static society. Moreover it was considered essential to foster the prosperity of the yeomanry from whose ranks were recruited the defenders of the realm: 'for that do we reckon that shepherds be but ill archers.' The apprehension was widespread that, if the depopulation of the countryside went on unchecked, there would come to pass 'a mere solitude and utter desolation to the whole realm furnished only with sheep and shepherds instead of good men, whereby it might be a prey to our enemies that first would set upon it.' Accordingly a number of statutes were passed in restraint of sheep-farming, enjoining that cultivated land converted into pasture should be restored to tillage. Nevertheless, while not altogether ineffective, they were powerless to stem the current of agrarian changes. Men who were bent on defying the law found evasion easy. It was futile to curtail the number of sheep which a grazier might keep, when 'some to colour the multitude of their sheep father them on their children, kinsfolk and servants.' The penalties against the conversion of arable into pasture could apparently be evaded by the simple expedient of driving a single furrow across the field. A contemporary writer recognized that legal devices were inadequate. 'It were hard to make a law therein, so many as have profit by that matter resisting it. And if such a law were made yet men would defraud the law.' His remedy was to increase the profit of corn-growing and diminish that of wool-growing by permitting the export of corn and prohibiting the export of wool. Otherwise 'the pasture shall ever encroach upon the tillage, for all the laws that ever can be made to the contrary.'

The wool produced in England was far from uniform in quality; it differed greatly according to the districts where it was raised. No less than fifty-one grades are enumerated in a fifteenth-century list (1454); the best came from parts of Shropshire and Leominster (in Herefordshire) and the Cotswolds. Hence to meet the requirements both of the home and foreign markets a complex mechanism was evolved; and the wool trade thus played the leading role in developing a commercial system which reproduced in essentials the features of an advanced economy. First, then, as to the home market. The manufacturer, unless he owned his own flock, obtained his supply of raw material in one of three ways—direct from the growers or through the agency of middlemen or from the yarn makers. The 'rich' clothier purchased his wool in the fleece from the farmers in the wool counties. The 'meaner' clothier relied upon the middlemen. The practice of the 'poor' clothier was to buy the spun yarn.

Hatred of the middlemen was deep-rooted; and the wool dealers, who bought wool from the growers and with 'greedy and covetous minds' (to use the picturesque phrase of the statute-book) sold it at enhanced prices to customers, came under the lash of condemnation which was visited upon all who sought to manipulate supplies and force up prices. Complaint was also made that the middlemen 'buying wool of several

counties and sorts as northern and western, pasture and fallow,
sell the same mingled and compounded to the clothier who—
not discovering nor able to single or separate again the different
wools—makes up a bad and ill-conditioned cloth, that mixed
wool not working alike in regard of its different qualities.'
Nevertheless, despite the criticisms levelled against the wool
dealers, it is evident that they served a useful purpose in the
economy of the wool textile industry. They linked up the manufacturing districts with their sources of supply. The short staple
grown in Norfolk, for example, was consumed in Yorkshire;
the long staple grown in Lincolnshire and Leicestershire was
worked up in Norwich; while 'Halifax men occupy fine wool
most out of Lincolnshire, and their coarse wool they sell to men
of Rochdale.'[1] Moreover the growers could not afford to sell
wool in small quantities to the poorer clothier and allow long
credit. The middlemen also enabled the clothier to buy his
wool ready sorted. A single fleece often contained several 'sorts'
of wool—perhaps a dozen or more; and it was the business of
the wool dealers to separate the various species to suit each
kind of cloth. This made it possible for the clothier to buy the
precise quantity and quality needed, and relieved him of the
obligation to purchase a whole fleece of which certain parts
might be useless to him. Hence the buying and sorting of wool
became a specialized function, the importance of which is
shown in the statement (made in an act of parliament in 1554)
that 'the perfect and principal ground of cloth-making is the
true sorting of wools.' Lastly, the fact that the middlemen
could dispose of the different qualities of wool to different
manufacturers must have tended to reduce the average price of
wool. It was, therefore, not altogether without justification
that the wool stapler was described[2] as 'the sheet anchor of
Great Britain.'

Laws in restraint of wool dealers were enacted in the fourteenth, fifteenth and sixteenth centuries. As early as 1390 it
was ordered that 'no Englishman buy any wool' other than

[1] The Privy Council was informed in 1621 that fine wool was taken to Worcester
and Somersetshire, coarse wool to Suffolk and Norfolk, and the worst wool to
Yorkshire, Lancashire and North Wales.
[2] In 1747.

manufacturers and merchant exporters, and the prohibition was repeated at intervals. Eventually it was found that complicated economic problems could not be solved by simple ethical rules, the attempt to eliminate the middleman being bound to fail in the absence of any other machinery to carry on his functions; and in the early seventeenth century internal free trade in wool was established and restrictions on wool dealers were swept away. The agitation against wool 'broggers' was renewed after the Revolution but Parliament declined to intervene: the grower might sell his wool 'to any chapman [dealer] he shall think fit to deal with.' The refusal indicated that the legislature, in this direction as in others, was throwing to the winds the cherished economic traditions which had inspired the industrial and commercial legislation of an earlier epoch.

We turn now to the foreign market. In the middle ages wool —'England's golden fleece,' and (as the poet Gower called it[1]) 'the goddess of merchants'—was the staple article of export and the main source of customs-revenue to which it contributed no less than three-fourths in the year 1421. Even in the tenth century wool was raised for sale abroad; while in later centuries it became the indispensable raw material of the great manufacturing cities of Flanders and Italy. The author of a pamphlet written in the fifteenth century, entitled *On England's Commercial Policy*, voiced the common opinion that no country was able to dispense with English wool; hence it provided the means by which 'we might rule and govern all Christian kings.' Edward III in particular had known how to use English wool as a bait to draw the large industrial towns of Flanders from their allegiance to the French king, and the mere threat to withhold supplies sufficed to humble the proud commons of Bruges, Ypres and Ghent.

The average cost of a sack of wool in the Cotswolds was eight pounds;[2] in addition there was a very heavy export duty;

[1] He apostrophizes it as 'the beautiful, the white, the delightful one. The love of you stings and binds, so that the hearts of those who make merchandise of you are not able to disengage themselves from you.'

[2] This was in the fifteenth century. Wool was exported in two forms—shorn wool (sold by the sack of 364 lb.) and wool-fells (sheepskins with the wool on them.)

accordingly the price overseas mounted high. None the less large quantities of English wool were sent to the Continent. During the last quarter of the thirteenth century and for two-thirds of the fourteenth century the number of sacks shipped by English and alien merchants exceeded 32,000. Subsequently the amount began to diminish rapidly: in the latter part of the fourteenth century it was reduced by more than a third. The decline and fall of England's export trade in wool are revealed in the following striking figures. The number of sacks averaged 19,300 in 1392-5, and 13,600 in 1410-15, and 8,000 in 1446-59; a slight recovery occurred near the end of Edward IV's reign when it rose to 9,000; during the first twelve years of Henry VIII's reign it was 8,600 and then it sank below 5,000. The downward trend continued until the Stuart dynasty ascended the throne, when the seal was put on this crucial transformation by an embargo on the shipment of wool. The counterpart of the shrinkage in the foreign consumption of England's raw materials was the growth in the foreign consumption of her manufactures.[1]

The export trade in wool in the middle ages was already organized on the lines of an advanced commercial system. The grower might sell the clip to foreign buyers, or to staplers who resold it to aliens abroad, or to woolmen who disposed of it at home either to staplers or to aliens.

The first stage, where the grower came into direct contact with foreign buyers (chiefly from the Netherlands and Italy), was general in the thirteenth century and it had not lapsed in the fifteenth century. The Italian merchants were accustomed to buy up the whole clip of a monastic house and to make contracts for a term of years. The nature of the arrangement is illustrated by a contract for the exclusive purchase of the wool crops of a Benedictine nunnery in Cleveland, Yorkshire. 'The prioress of Arden was attached to answer to Coppus Cotenni on a plea that she do render to him ten pounds which she owes to him and unjustly detains; and whereupon the said Coppus proffered a certain writing which he says is the deed of Margaret' (a former prioress), acknowledging that the prioress and

[1] See Part II.

convent of Arden have sold to Coppus and his 'fellows, merchants of the society of the Friscobaldi of Florence, all the wool [of the house of Arden for 1291] and for nine years next following fully completed, namely, every sack for eleven marks and a half.[1] And the aforesaid wool shall be well prepared and weighed according to the use and custom of the house aforesaid without cooked and black guard, grey scab, clacked and all vile fleeces.[2] And that the aforesaid merchants shall pay to the said prioress and convent in hand as earnest money ten pounds of good sterlings, whereof the aforesaid ten pounds in the last year shall be fully allowed to the same merchants. And the aforesaid merchants shall pay to them in hand as earnest money ten pounds every year [within an appointed term], and the whole residue in consideration of the aforesaid wool the said merchants shall pay to the said prioress and convent at the issue and delivery of the wool aforesaid. And they shall find sarpler-makers and packers of the said wool at their expense. And the said prioress and convent at their expense shall carry the said wool to Thorp to the wool-house of Byland [a Cistercian nunnery in Cleveland, Yorkshire] at the feast of the Nativity of S. John the Baptist [1291], and so from year to year until the ten years shall be fully completed. And for this they bind themselves and their successors and all their goods. Dated at Arden [1284].'

The export of wool entered upon its second stage when the staplers, who were native merchants engaged in oversea trade, became the intermediaries between the growers and the foreign buyers. The third stage was reached when the woolmen, engaged in home trade, were interposed between the growers on one side and the exporters (staplers and aliens) on the other. The growers disposed of the clip to the woolmen, who resold it to the exporters. Economic stages, however, overlap; and both staplers and aliens continued to buy direct from the growers as well as from the woolmen. Eventually the woolmen drew most of the business into their own hands, for they offered many advantages over the growers. They spared the exporters

---

[1] A mark = 13s. 4d.
[2] This means the removal of the inferior parts and of the refuse.

the trouble of distant journeys; they made the mechanism of commerce more flexible since it was their function to furnish the exact quantities and qualities required by their customers; and they conceded long credit. Transactions throughout were conducted on a credit basis. The woolmen gave credit to the staplers, who in turn gave credit to alien dealers though a portion of the purchase price—often a third—fell due immediately; even the growers sometimes allowed credit to the woolmen, while at other times the purchasers paid them a substantial sum in advance and the residue on delivery. The relations between growers, woolmen and staplers, are depicted in a transaction (1482) involving the Celys a fifteenth-century firm of merchant exporters. A woolman, who had contracted to supply the Celys with wool at a stipulated price, discovered that he had 'misjudged the market' and could not buy at the price which he had anticipated; moreover the growers were requiring him to pay ready money. His letter to the staplers reads thus: 'Sir, I made a bargain with you at that season, the which I would I had slept the whiles, for . . . I trusted that I should not a [have] bought their wool above 13s. 8d. a tod, and now I cannot buy their wool under 14s. and 13s. 6d. a tod; the price is, that I buy at, above that I sold you right much; and to reckon the refuse I shall lose by my troth a noble or 10s. in every sarpler. And, as my troth help me, and they must have ready money by and by—they that were wont to leave in my hand most part of their money—now they must needs have all their money. And now I must trust to your courtesy, and I pray you consider this well as ye may have my service, for I must trust to you that I may have the £200 that ye said I should not have till November. I pray as heartily as I can that ye make it ready within fourteen days after Michaelmas, or else I am hotly shamed.'

After the wool had been purchased, it was taken from the interior to the coast on pack-horses; then it was put on board different ships as a measure of security, whereby merchants ran less risk of losing the total consignment. When the wool reached Calais, it was the common practice for the oversea buyers to pay a certain sum in cash and give bills for the rest. The date

at which the bills fell due (that is, the period of the credit) was
a matter for bargaining; and interest was charged by the device
of varying the rate of exchange.[1] The discounting of bills by
'assigning' or transferring them was also usual, so that the
trade custom of circulating bills from one creditor to another is
at least five hundred years old. The stapler, on receiving his
money, was confronted with the problem of bringing it home.
There were three alternative methods—one was to carry back
gold and silver; the second was to buy goods abroad and import
them into England; the third was to purchase a bill of exchange
drawn upon a merchant importer in London and payable in
English money. The government vainly endeavoured to confine
the staplers to the first course alone. The 'Partition Ordinance'
issued in 1429 laid down that no credit was to be allowed; that
the seller of wool abroad must receive full payment in gold and
silver at the time of the transaction; and that one-third was to
be taken to the mint at Calais for coining into English money
(at one time more silver was minted in Calais than in London).
The Ordinance remained in operation for the space of fourteen
years.

The whole structure of the export trade in wool came to rest
in the later middle ages upon the institution known as the
staple. The history of the English staple is largely the history of
English commerce in the fourteenth and fifteenth centuries.
The staple was a depot where traders deposited their wares; it
was a continuous mart at which commodities were bought and
sold, just as the fair was a periodical mart. The underlying
principle of the staple system—which ultimately was a creation
of the state rather than a private enterprise, though its control
was vested in the hands of a chartered company known as the
Merchants of the Staple—was to regulate the stream of commerce and force it into defined channels. The staple served as
a centre of distribution to which merchandise was carried in
the first instance and there exposed for sale. When it exercised
a monopoly and was made compulsory for traders it prevented
free trade, but was recommended to the government by certain

---

[1] The rate at which foreign currencies were exchanged into English money
could be adjusted to cover interest.

fiscal and political advantages. Its primary purpose was to facilitate the collection of the customs-revenue. It was devised as part of the financial machinery—both to prevent evasion of toll on the part of those who conveyed English wool abroad *furtim et occulte*, and to guard against the fraudulent malpractices of collectors who were accused of grave offences in the discharge of their duties. At the same time it was made easier to enforce a recognized standard of quality by bringing the exported goods under the direct control and supervision of the royal officials. The staple also served a political purpose as an instrument of diplomacy by which to conciliate friends and intimidate enemies. Foreign courts intrigued for its possession and it was eagerly sought after by France, Holland, Flanders, Artois and Brabant. Eventually, after Calais became an English outpost, the staple was established there and for two centuries remained the chief centre of our oversea trade in wool.

Occasionally this oversea trade was interrupted when an embargo was placed by the government on the export of a highly prized commodity. As far back as the thirteenth century it was ordered that 'the wool of the country should be worked up in England and not sold to foreigners;' and a member of parliament declared in 1621 that 'at least' thirty statutes had revived the prohibition. But the embargo was usually short-lived; and even when nominally in force it was evaded by the purchase of licences, granted for revenue purposes, allowing raw materials to be sent out of the country. The growth of the woollen and worsted industries, however, enlarged the home market for English wool and caused a natural shrinkage of the export trade which was described in 1601 as 'almost wholly decayed.' After the loss of Calais the staplers still carried on operations yet they no longer enjoyed 'an assured place of residence' abroad; and the system of licences and heavy duties handicapped legitimate exporters, while it encouraged an illicit trade which brought in no revenue. The fact that the normal and revenue-producing channels of the trade were thus drying up facilitated an orientation of policy; and in the seventeenth century the transportation of wool beyond the sea was forbidden not as a temporary expedient but as a permanent feature of the commercial system known in history as the mercantile system. James I—'upon information of the setting up of clothing and drapery in the United Provinces, and the exportation of great quantities of wool into those parts'—issued several proclamations for the 'restraining of the wool of this realm from exportation.' They were repeated by Charles I and Cromwell and embodied in an act of parliament at the Restoration. Thus the industrial revolution of the fifteenth century, which had been due to the growth of wool textiles,[1] was followed in its turn by a commercial revolution in the seventeenth century. The manufacturers, who fought against free trade in raw materials, had now proved strong enough to overcome the opposition of the landed interest and force their wishes upon the government. Henceforth for two centuries it was the avowed aim of a thorough-going policy of protection to keep native wool within the country. This reflected a momentous change in economic statesmanship.

In spite of all its efforts to check the export of wool, reinforced by naval and military support, the government was unable to repress a clandestine and illicit trade which sprang up immediately. Among other places the people of Faversham are said to have grown 'monstrous rich' by 'that wicked trade;' and Kent and Sussex seemed at one period a smugglers' paradise. The smugglers brought back with them cargoes of silk, lace and liquors. Their methods are described in a number of pamphlets written by William Carter, for over a quarter of a century their indefatigable adversary. 'First, in Romney Marsh in Kent where the greatest part of rough wool is exported from England, put aboard French shallops by night, ten or twenty men well armed to guard it; some other parts there are as in Sussex, Hampshire and Essex, the same methods may be used but not so conveniently. The same for combed wool from Canterbury; they will carry it ten or fifteen miles at night towards the sea with the like guard as before.' As a measure of precaution while the wool was afloat, it was pressed into barrels with screws, and then the barrels were 'washed

[1] See Part II.

over with brine-water' in order that they might pass for beef
or herrings. 'These barrels are not put on board in ports where
they are liable to be examined, but conveyed into creeks from
whence they are shipped off.'[1] According to one statement
(1703), wool in its raw state was worth in Ireland fourpence
per pound and combed wool tenpence: in France the first was
sold for half-a-crown a pound, the second for five and sixpence
or six shillings—'so that the temptation is really almost too
great to be withstood especially by such who only measure
their consciences by their gain.' This estimate of the profits
made in the smuggling trade, if not exaggerated, points to
exceptional circumstances though in time of war the risks of
the enterprise were always enhanced. A more moderate
calculation represented the profit at threepence a pound on
English wool, which amounted to 50 or 60 per cent. in regard
to the capital employed 'in that illicit trade.'

The wool smugglers were called *owlers*. Their desperate
character was shown in the hardihood with which they attacked
the coast-guardsmen, who were often 'obliged as it were to
stand still and see the wool carried off before their faces, not
daring to meddle—none dare meddle with them without five
files of soldiers.' The severity of the penalties did not deter
those who boasted that 'if a gallows was set up every quarter
of a mile, yet they would carry the wool off;' and they 'readily
risked their necks for twelvepence a day.' The sympathies of
the local population, who in some places were almost all
engaged in the owling-trade, were never in doubt; the municipal authorities declined to assist the officers appointed to
prevent the export of wool; and the latter—for the payment of
whose salaries or even the expenses involved in seizing and
prosecuting offenders no provision was apparently made other
than the fines inflicted on smugglers who were caught—became
negligent and corrupt. The repression of smuggling in these
difficult circumstances proved hazardous in the extreme. This
is illustrated by an exciting incident in which William Carter
was concerned at Romney Marsh in 1688. 'Having procured

---

[1] Another device was to manufacture woollen goods fraudulently, so that the
wool was easily unravelled.

the necessary warrants he repaired to Romney Marsh where he seized eight or ten men who were carrying the wool on horses' backs to be shipped, and desired the mayor of Romney to commit them. The mayor, wishing no doubt to live a peaceful life among his neighbours, admitted them to bail. Carter and his assistants retired to Lydd but that town was made too hot to hold them—they were attacked at night; adopting the advice of the mayor's son [whom they afterwards suspected to be in league with the smugglers], the next day December 13 came towards Rye. They were pursued by some fifty armed horsemen till they got to Camber Point; so fast were they followed that they could not get their horses over Guildford Ferry; but, luckily, some ships' boats gave them assistance so that the riders got safe into the town which had been put into much fear.' On another occasion William Carter arrested a smuggler at Folkestone, 'but the women of the town came out of their houses and gathered up stones upon the beach, which they flung about my ears so violently that having no help I was forced to quit my prisoner hardly escaping myself.'

The smuggling of wool attracted considerable attention; and a proclamation issued by James II denounced those who 'by open force and violence with armed companies of men' conveyed wool beyond the seas. After the Revolution fresh legislation was enacted. The severity of the penalty was modified (1696) in order not to deter the prosecution of offenders; and ships were appointed (1698) 'constantly to cruise on the coasts of England and Ireland' to seize vessels exporting wool; two years later the Admiralty reported that they had not taken a single vessel while they had lost two of their own and expected to lose others, and the cost involved amounted to £2,400 a month. The clothiers complained in 1701 that 'notwithstanding this kingdom is at great charges in maintaining vessels and men to prevent the exportation of wool, yet within these two years many thousand packs of wool have been exported into France and other foreign parts.' The government, unable to devise any remedy, transferred the responsibility to Parliament; and the speech from the throne (1702) recommended the legislature to 'find time to consider of some better and more effectual method to prevent the exportation of wool, and to improve that manufacture which is of great consequence to the whole kingdom.' Many schemes were propounded for preventing the transportation of wool. The favourite expedient, mooted early in the seventeenth century and widely canvassed in the next century, was to establish official registers to 'keep sight of all wool from its being shorn till it was completely manufactured.' A local scheme was put into operation by the act of 1698 which instituted a registry in Kent and Sussex. It provided that all owners of wool in these counties within ten miles of the sea 'shall be obliged to give an exact account in writing, within three days after the shearing thereof,' of the number and the weight of the fleeces and the name of the person to whom it is disposed and the place to which it is carried. A proposal for a national scheme was rejected by the Commissioners for Trade and Plantations in 1732 on the ground that it would be very expensive and involve a 'multiplicity of accounts.' Nevertheless a few years later the idea was revived; and in response to a petition from 'the lord mayor, aldermen and commons' of London expressing 'unspeakable grief' at 'so great and crying an evil,' the House of Commons passed a resolution (1741) declaring that 'a public register of the wool grown in Great Britain and Ireland is the most effectual method for preventing the exportation thereof to foreign parts.' No machinery, however, was instituted for the purpose and smuggling went on unchecked. 'Long experience hath demonstrated,' it was observed (1680), 'that the mere prohibiting of the exportation of wool is but a cobweb.' Adam Smith a century later remarked: 'It is exported, it is well known, in great quantities.'

It is a striking testimony to the importance of the wool textile industry that the law forbidding the export of wool remained on the statute-book more than a hundred and fifty years. One result was to create a rivalry of interests between agriculture and industry, which in one form or another has ever since been a feature of our economic system. The manufacturers' demand for cheap raw materials and cheap food brought them into conflict with the farmers over the first in the

c

seventeenth and eighteenth centuries and over the second in the nineteenth century. Hence they found it necessary to exercise the utmost vigilance in warding off attacks upon a privilege which had been wrested from the rulers of the state in the teeth of bitter opposition on the part of the landed interest. The graziers raised a violent agitation against their confinement to the home market, and an interminable argument was carried on in an unceasing stream of pamphlets and broadsheets.

The embargo on wool originated in the desire to ensure abundant supplies for the native clothiers who claimed a natural right to monopolize the use of native products. Yet jealousy of continental rivals, rather than any apprehension of a scarcity, became the dominating motive that inspired the determination to exclude them from the English wool market. James I's proclamation of 1614, which inaugurated the change in commercial policy, was intended to check the growth of the Dutch woollen industry, 'so that we may not be killed with arrows from our own quiver;' and later, French competition came to be greatly dreaded owing to the cheapness of French labour. Two propositions were accepted as axiomatic. One was that trade depressions were caused or aggravated by the export of wool—'whereby the stranger's wheel is set going.' The other was that foreign competition could be extinguished by refusing to supply other countries with raw materials. Accordingly the discussion centred on the question whether English wool was indispensable for the continental textile industries. It was sometimes maintained that 'there is not a piece of broadcloth or new drapery made in France without the help of our wool,' one pack of the latter being worked up with two of their own. Spanish wool, though fine, was short and required an admixture of English or Irish wool to make fine thin cloth: other kinds of wool, German or French, were so coarse that the cloth was not 'merchandisable' unless mixed with British wool. The long staple or 'combing' wool, in particular, was claimed to be 'absolutely necessary in some of the French manufactures.' The prohibition of wool was therefore defended on economic and political grounds alike. If we manufactured all our wool, ran the economic argument, 'we should have the markets of the known world to ourselves and at our own price.' If we cut off France from supplies of English and Irish wool, ran the political argument, our national enemy would be unable to carry on her manufactures since bricks cannot be made without straw, and we should be saved from 'falling a sacrifice to universal monarchy and arbitrary power.' 'Our Fathers bravely pulled down the exorbitant power of France at the expense of their blood and their treasure, but never thought of the way to give her a more deadly wound than she could receive by the loss of ten battles and twice as many towns.' The export of wool, protested the manufacturers, would be an unparalleled disaster: it would 'change the current of their wealth, destroy their industry and enterprise, deprive the poor of their employment, add to the poor rates, and diminish the rental of the land.' 'Ere the next generation,' cried a panic-stricken 'Cheshire Weaver' after recounting the fatal consequences attending the smuggling of wool, 'England will be no more.'

The advocates of free trade on their part endeavoured to show the folly of a system in which wool, the 'coveted vineyard,' was 'watched with as much care and jealousy as the Golden Apples of the Hesperides.' The policy of protection was denounced as an evil legacy of the Great Rebellion; it was the work of the Commonwealth party, which had 'been assisted in the Civil Wars by great numbers of the wool-workmen who liked much better to rob and plunder for half-a-crown a day than toil at a melancholy work for sixpence a day,' and which prohibited the export of wool in order 'to encourage and reward them and to weaken the gentry.' The embargo on wool was condemned by the wool growers on three grounds—it was unnecessary; it served to defeat its own ends; and it was injurious to the landed interest.

The leading exponent of the argument that free trade in wool would not harm the English manufacturers was John Smith whose book,[1] though written with a polemical purpose, is a valuable storehouse of historical material. Of this work it was

[1] *Chronicon Rusticum-Commerciale: Or Memoirs of Wool* (1747).

said by an agriculturist that it 'ought to be printed in letters of gold.' The author sought to combat the notion that foreign nations could not carry on their textile industries without British wool. England and Ireland, he affirmed, did not possess the vaunted superiority in wool: we therefore gained no benefit from prohibiting its transportation. Smith was not the first to employ this argument: more than a century earlier Misselden had denied that foreign manufacturers could not make cloth without our wool. The tradition that English wool was the best in the world had acquired almost the sanctity of a dogma; yet the only kind of wool sometimes admitted by the free traders to be peculiar to England was 'combing' wool.

> If any wool peculiar to our isle
> Is giv'n by nature, 'tis the comber's lock;
> The soft, the snow-white and the long-grown flake.

Moreover the best English cloth now contained a large admixture of Spanish wool; and our dependence on Spain deprived us of our former monopoly and placed us on the same footing as other countries.

In the next place the embargo on wool depressed its price in England, and the low price encouraged illicit trading since the 'unnatural artificial cheapness' of the raw materials at home made it worth while to smuggle them abroad. The fact that wool here was kept below the 'natural value' served as 'an advantage, in the nature of a premium, to the exporter of woollen goods; yet at the same time it afforded equally a premium for the runnage of wool.' 'This in a word,' said Smith, 'is the mainspring of the owling trade.' As Sir Josiah Child pointed out: 'They that can give the best price for a commodity shall never fail to have it.'

There remained the final plea that it was the duty of the nation to preserve the landed class, the 'masters and proprietors of the foundation of all the wealth in this nation,' who maintained great families, bore the burden of taxation, and filled all the magistracies and public offices. The spoliation of the landed interest was deemed the more indefensible because it was 'the most considerable national interest' and wool was

its 'principal' support. It was therefore on the ground of in-
equity that the wool growers denounced 'the oppression which
the grazier suffers under this iniquitous system of monopoly.'
They asked: 'If he that combs, dyes, weaves, works, or exports
wool, thrives—why should he that grows it be impoverished?
Why must the grazier be the only sufferer, where all other
dealers in wool are gainers by it?' The manufacturers replied
that the welfare of the landed and industrial interests 'mutually
depend on each other.' The value of land depended on trade
inasmuch as a prosperous trade increased the demand for
agricultural produce such as corn, beef, mutton, etc.; hence
the farmers were compensated in other directions if their wool
sold at a lower price at home than it would fetch abroad.
Smith retorted that the embargo on the export trade in wool
might benefit the export trade in cloth, but it certainly created
'a monopoly against the grower;' and 'whether thus robbing
Peter to enrich Paul is of any real public benefit? that is the
point to be considered.' Arthur Young was conspicuous for the
vigour with which he repudiated the alleged identity of interests between agriculture and industry: 'Let us hear no more
from woolmen of the prosperity of land and manufactures
being the same.' He bitterly deplored that 'the gentlemen of
the landed interest have quietly laid themselves down to be
fleeced by the woolmen, like their sheep;' and he roundly
declared that 'the sweets of a monopoly of their raw materials'
had made the woollen manufacturers indolent and devoid of
the 'ardour of enterprise' or the 'spirit of invention.' In spite of
their arguments the efforts of growers to secure a limited
export of wool proved unsuccessful; and in 1788 the penalties
were made even more stringent than before—amidst great
rejoicings in the industrial areas where the bells were set ringing.
The severity of the penalties imposed at one period or another
called forth Adam Smith's acid reflection that the laws, 'which
the clamour of our merchants and manufacturers has extorted
from the legislature for the support of their own absurd and
oppressing monopolies, [may be said] like the laws of Draco
to be all written in blood.'

We have seen that for two centuries it was a leading principle of English economic policy to prevent the transportation of wool abroad: but after the Napoleonic wars a new departure ushered in another revolutionary change. Men of vision, seeking to break down artificial commercial barriers and establish free trade, lent a willing ear to the plea of the farmers that, as they were not allowed to export their wool to foreign markets, they ought in compensation to enjoy the monopoly of the home market. Accordingly the manufacturers were offered the choice of the free export of native wool or a heavy duty on imported wool. Each alternative was equally distasteful to them. They still persisted in their belief that 'should foreigners be able to procure English wool to mix with that of their own growth, the exportation of woollen goods from this country would immediately cease.' Nevertheless they could not reconcile themselves to a tax on imported wool of which they now used large quantities. Experiments were tried in the hope of producing wool in the British Isles as fine as the wool of Spain, and George III imported from Spain several rams and ewes of the notable Negretti breed. In addition sheep of the merino breed were introduced here; but the agriculturists were disappointed in their efforts to raise wool equal in fineness to Spanish or Saxon wool, and so they pressed upon the government the taxation of foreign wool. 'The increase in the growth of wool of the Spanish race upon the Continent calls imperiously,' they declared, 'for some parliamentary interference to protect our wool growers from being driven out of our own market.' The agitation bore fruit (1819) in the imposition of a heavy duty on imported wool. The government soon offered to repeal the tax[1] if no opposition were made to the export of British wool; and the manufacturers, impaled on the horns of a dilemma, yielded to force of circumstances (1824).

This complete reversal of our commercial policy was accompanied by, and indeed was largely the result of, changes in the sources of our wool supply. The dominating factor in the situation was the increasing dependence of English

---

[1] American historians hold that this was to offset the protection given to woollen manufacturers in the United States under the tariff of 1824.

manufacturers upon wool grown abroad. In the second half of the eighteenth century we imported approximately $2\frac{1}{2}$ million pounds of wool, at the beginning of the nineteenth century 8 m., at the middle 74 m., before the first world war about 500 m., before the second up to 700 m. The sources from which these vast quantities were obtained are worth noticing. At first the main source was Spain, whose wool was brought to our shores at least as early as the fourteenth century and was described in the seventeenth century as 'of important concernment.' It amounted to $5\frac{1}{2}$ m. in 1802 and to $8\frac{3}{4}$ m. in 1818— the high-water mark of the Spanish supply which fell to $3\frac{1}{2}$ m. in 1820, to $1\frac{1}{2}$ m. in 1830 and to $\frac{1}{2}$ m. in 1850. Another source was Germany from which we drew 3 m. in 1815 and 26 m. in 1830; the figure dropped to 22 m. in 1840 and to 9 m. in 1850. The most important source in the nineteenth and twentieth centuries was neither Spain nor Germany but Australia. In 1820 she sent us 100,000 pounds; a decade later the volume had increased twentyfold and two decades later a hundredfold; in 1850 it was 39 m. and in 1913 (with New Zealand) it was 446 m. Eventually something like four-fifths of gross imports came from the Empire.

England is not only a principal market for wool but she is herself a leading exporter. After it was legalized in the third decade of the nineteenth century (1824) the export trade in home-grown wool steadily expanded though at a slower rate. In 1820 about 35,000 pounds had been conveyed abroad; the amount rose to 143,000 (1826), $1\frac{3}{4}$ m. (1828), 4 m. (1832), 12 m. (1850), 33 m. (1938).[1] Of the various agricultural products which in former ages we shipped abroad (corn, butter, cheese and the rest), wool remains—as it has done for a thousand years except when it was legally prohibited in the seventeenth and eighteenth centuries—almost the sole and certainly the most considerable. However the major portion of the home clip, which fluctuates within a wide range above and below 110 million pounds annually,[2] is retained for domestic purposes.

---

[1] Greasy basis (*i.e.* unscoured). On a clean basis it was 30 m. lb. in 1938. There are wide variations in different years. British wool is largely used for carpets and rugs.

[2] Greasy basis. In 1951 it had fallen to 90 m. lb. (approximate).

Thus England, like the United States, is at once a large producer as well as a large importer of wool. The two countries
share the distinction that they grow as well as manufacture
wool on an extensive scale, yet now both rely mainly on
imported wool.

The increasing dependence of the woollen and worsted
industries upon imported wool, and the removal of the embargo
on the export of home-grown wool, were closely connected
with an epoch-making change in the character of English sheep.
The breeding of larger sheep in place of the 'ancient small
breed' produced a deterioration in the quality of native wool.
As late as the sixteenth century the Venetian envoy had
claimed that 'Spanish wool cannot be compared [with
England's] very fine and most excellent wool.' At the end of
the next century the position was reversed, and it came to be
generally recognized that English wool was no longer superior
to Spanish wool—'we must submit to Spain in the utmost
curiosity of fineness.' It was said: 'So long as Englishmen
are fond of fat mutton they must not expect to grow fine
wool.'

This notable development received a marked impulse from
the renowned experiments of Robert Bakewell, who in the latter
part of the eighteenth century set to work to breed sheep for
the meat market.[1] Although Bakewell was a great pioneer in the
technique of stock breeding he was not the first in the field.
Even in the thirteenth century rams were introduced from one
part of the country to another in order to improve local breeds;
and the 'changing of rams of late years' attracted the attention
of a writer in 1739. The improvements effected in the native
sheep were not only due to careful selection for breeding
purposes; other factors were better care of the flock, superior
management of the pastures, feeding of root crops and clover
which solved the problem of winter diet. A wool stapler (Luccock) writing in 1805 remarked: 'There are not many counties
which can boast of such rapid improvement in its fleece as

---

[1] An eighteenth-century geologist, who was a namesake of Robert Bakewell, was
once asked 'whether he was related to the Mr. Bakewell who invented sheep.'

Norfolk has witnessed. Even in living memory its wool was kempy, rough and thin. But the introduction of a new mode of husbandry furnished a larger supply of food. Wool has risen to more than seven times its former value.'[1] Robert Bakewell (1725–95) concentrated his energies on long wool sheep, the Old Leicesters—'large rough animals'—now in his hands turned into New Leicesters which spread their blood more widely than any other breed. Another improver, John Ellman (1753–1832), devoted his efforts to short wool sheep, the Southdowns which 'sent out colonies that are gradually producing an alteration in the short woolled sheep of the surrounding counties' (Luccock). Both Bakewell and Ellman would doubtless have endorsed the view expressed in a later generation that the production of improved breeds of sheep was 'a work of human skill worthy of being classed with the great inventions.' While the attention paid to the carcass was rewarded with mutton of choice quality, the wool stapler was complaining that 'we are too indifferent respecting the fleece.' The momentous change had been accomplished: the English breeder had grown more interested in the flesh of the sheep than in the wool.

At the present day England continues to send abroad wool: in addition she now sends sheep. She excels in the production of 'mutton' breeds, and many thousands of pedigree sheep have served as crossing sires to transmit their blood in numerous parts of the globe. It is not, indeed, generally recognized that the British Isles have not only exported men all over the world but also sheep.

For England's pre-eminence in her own pastoral sphere there are substantial reasons. The report of the United States Tariff Board stated in 1912: English breeds 'are the product of a cool and equable climate; the highly specialized product of a land where rich grasses or succulent forage are never lacking; the product of a system of close handling such as has no real counterpart upon the farms and ranches of our own country; a class of animals the pride and boast of a race of men with whom the art of careful shepherding is hereditary. Bred locally

---

[1] The sharp rise in price was also due to the inflation of currency during the Napoleonic wars.

for generations with certain variations of type, each apparently is best adapted in its pure-bred form to some particular soil or elevation that claims it for its own.'[1] The report added that almost every county had its own peculiar breed. Several centuries ago it was remarked that 'in every shire in England there is variety of sorts and prices according to the pastures;' and we noticed above that a fifteenth-century document listed over fifty grades. The wide range of elevation (high land can be utilized for grazing), soil and climatic conditions favoured the production of types suited to the locality. Hence the existence of more than a score and a half breeds and innumerable cross-breds with some corresponding variation in the wool. However we can distinguish three main species—long wool, short wool and mountain. The long wool species include the Leicester, Lincoln, Cotswolds and Kent. The Leicester, which is among the oldest of improved breeds, has been widely used for crossing with other breeds; while the Lincoln is the largest sheep in England if not in the world. The short wool species comprise in particular the downs. The Southdown (formerly called the Sussex down) gained renown for producing the finest fleece in this country, and its mutton is 'the standard of the world.' The Southdown, together with the Dorset down, Hampshire down, Oxford down, Shropshire and Suffolk, are 'the mutton sheep of the world *par excellence*' (these phrases come from an official American report). They thus constitute the 'dual purpose' sheep which is now the predominant aim of breeders, the combination of fine texture wool with high grade mutton. The mountain species are hardy sheep in Scotland, Wales and certain English counties, which yield flesh of good quality.

England carries more sheep in proportion to her size than any other industrialized nation; and she is surpassed only by New Zealand in the density of sheep per square mile, and by barely more than half-a-dozen other countries in the total number of sheep which normally does not fall much short of thirty millions.[2]

[1] *A Dictionary of Commerce* (1742) attributed the fineness of English wool to excellent pastures and fine short grass, coupled with mild winters which made it possible to keep sheep in the fields all the year round.

[2] An eighteenth-century estimate (1774) for England was 10 or 12 m. In 1939 the United Kingdom had 27 m. It fell considerably during the second world war. In 1951 it was 20 m. Many pastures have been ploughed up.

The existence of a considerable sheep industry in a highly industrialized region is explained by the character of English agriculture. The system of mixed farming or convertible husbandry—the combination of arable cultivation and production of livestock—ensures the ubiquity of the sheep. The latter, indeed, occupy a vital place in our agrarian economy. They are especially valuable for preserving the fertility of light and sandy soil by treading it down and manuring it. This indispensable consolidation and fertilizing make possible heavier and better harvests of grain crops. Land which is no longer virgin, and for hundreds of years has yielded food, needs to repair the loss of essential substances. The practice of folding sheep goes back to the middle ages. The tenure of 'fold-soke,' by which a tenant was bound to do suit at his lord's fold, appears frequently in Domesday Book. It was in general the mark of a free status when a man was 'fold-worthy,' that is, he could send his cattle to his own fold or to that of the village. Yet fold service even on the part of freemen was not unknown. Thus the abbot of Kingeswood was bound to find a fold of over two hundred sheep upon the land of the lord of Berkeley from May to November.

CHAPTER THREE

Merino and Crossbred Wool

ENGLISH SHEEP of the 'mutton' type constitute one of the two main breeds which have spread their blood the world over; the other is the Spanish merinos, whose fleece inherited the prestige formerly enjoyed by the 'ancient small breed' of English sheep.

It is generally believed that merinos take their name from a Moorish tribe the Beni-Merines, which brought them to Spain from North Africa in the second half of the twelfth century, although the name itself was not commonly applied until five hundred years later. The rigour of the winter in the northern uplands of Spain gave rise to the annual migrations of sheep. Branded with the mark of their owner and under their own herdsmen, they trekked to the southern plains in September and retraced their steps in April. The distance was often considerable: some covered four to five hundred miles in their journey southwards to 'pastures new,' but others less than half. Along the sheep-walks specially provided for them they might traverse fifteen or eighteen miles a day though across the open country only five or six miles. Lambs were born after they reached the southern plains, and the wool clipping took place in the course of their return. It was these migratory flocks which Don Quixote encountered in one of the best known episodes of the dismal knight of La Mancha. The fact that each journey might occupy a whole month kept the sheep hardy and in good condition and increased the fineness of the wool.

At an early period there originated the practice of holding gatherings of the sheep owners and herdsmen in the locality to consider matters of common interest, for instance, hiring shepherds, fixing wages and determining the ownership of stray animals. These assemblies were the local 'mestas' and out of them developed a powerful national organization which controlled the pastoral industry of Spain. In 1273 Alfonso the Learned incorporated 'all of the shepherds of Castile' in one 'Honourable Assembly of the Mesta of the Shepherds,' which he endowed with a charter. Its sphere was restricted to the kingdom of Castile until the late seventeenth century when it was extended to Aragon. For over five hundred years this famous gild wielded authority over the merino flocks of Spain, which comprised between two and a half and three million head of sheep. It was concerned exclusively with the wool not with the flesh of the animal. Like the mediaeval gilds of England it acted on behalf of its members—although it controlled production it owned neither herds nor pastures; although it controlled marketing it did not engage in selling. It endured down to 1836 when it was transformed into a Stock Owners' Association. The migratory sheep still persist in Spain yet for distant pastures they no longer march on foot but (*tempora mutantur*) travel by rail.

The importance attached to the pastoral industry in Spain is shown by a remark made early in the seventeenth century: 'There is no grandee of Spain who has so many judges and sheriffs to defend him as has the sheep.' In the later middle ages the existence of an international trade in Spanish wool had already become an important factor in European economy. Its export abroad finds a place in English customs accounts (for example in 1303), and it helped to 'sustain the commons of Flanders' when they were deprived of English wool. While Spain, unlike England, permitted the export of wool, she prohibited the export of sheep; but the embargo was partially lifted in the eighteenth century. Merinos were introduced into Sweden in the first half; into Saxony, Hungary, France, England, South Africa and Australia in the second half; subsequently into Russia, the United States and South America. Thus, like English sheep, merinos became 'cosmopolitan animals' extensively distributed over the face of the globe. Yet to-day pure merinos are not to be found in England, France or Germany; they have been crossed with the indigenous stocks. A writer in 1805 remarked: 'A few spirited individuals have combined with various English breeds the blood of the Spanish race and by that means obtained a staple hitherto unequalled among English wools, yet those flocks are small and widely dispersed.' Merino wool is still raised in one European country, Spain, but in quality it has been surpassed by countries of the southern hemisphere. The proportion of merino wool on the eve of the second world war was as high as 95 per cent. of total production in South Africa, 85 per cent. in Australia, and 50 per cent. in the United States.[1] The numerical preponderance of merino wool[2] in areas which concentrate on producing the finest wool rather than on flesh is due to its superior fineness, softness, strength, elasticity and felting properties.

The merino sheep is hardy and thrives in inhospitable and dry districts (it is apparently unsuited for the moist climate of England). It is essentially a 'wool' sheep with a dense fine fleece, and the flesh is less palatable than that of a 'mutton' sheep. Accordingly in the last decade of the nineteenth century began the trend towards a 'dual purpose' animal which might serve both for the table and for apparel. This is achieved by crossing the small lean merinos with the large fat English breeds suited to the purpose. The offsprings of the mating are known as crossbreds,[3] which mingle the blood of two historic strains that independently or in combination continue to dominate the wool production of the world as they have done for many centuries. The highly important movement in which crossbreds are displacing merinos has proceeded furthest in New Zealand and South America. They constitute outstanding examples of regions which have ceased to concentrate primarily on wool in order to combine wool with meat.[4] Crossbred wool on the eve of the second world war accounted for 98 per cent. of the New Zealand clip, 88 per cent. of the Argentine clip, 87 per

[1] The first two percentages have markedly declined.
[2] It is estimated that approximately one-third of the total world clip is classed as merino wool.
[3] The term crossbred is also applied to sheep whose wool has the quality termed crossbred, namely, the medium type.
[4] The growth of crossbred wool was also stimulated by a change of fashion when fine worsteds supplanted fine broadcloth. The increased demand for smooth worsteds could now be met owing to improvements in combing machinery. Henceforth the latter could use wool of shorter staple and was no longer restricted to long wool, of which the supply was limited.

cent. of the Uruguay clip, and 50 per cent. of the United States clip.[1]

We must now sketch in outline the history of these two famous breeds—merinos and crossbreds—in countries far remote from Europe, where they have prospered and multiplied exceedingly in response to the ever-growing needs of the human race for apparel and food.

In the eighteenth century the belief had been widespread that the sources of our wool supply were strictly limited. Indeed it was advanced as an argument against the introduction of machinery that 'it is not possible to increase the raw material beyond the present quantity. The growth of wool is definite'— hence there was no possibility of an extension of woollen manufactures to compensate operatives for the loss of employment in the manual processes. The potentialities of the southern hemisphere in the field of wool production were virtually unknown at the end of the eighteenth century, although a few men had a vision of the future. When the first fleet sailed from England for New South Wales in 1787 it took in some sheep at the Cape of Good Hope: these were native sheep valuable only for mutton. The early experiences of the colonists did not prove encouraging. 'In 1788 Governor Phillip had the mortification to learn that five ewes and a lamb had been destroyed at a farm, supposed to have been killed by dogs belonging to the natives. This to the happy inhabitants of Great Britain may appear a circumstance too trivial to record, but to the founders of a new colony it would be of magnitude sufficient to be by them deemed a public calamity.' The next year Captain Waterhouse was sent from Australia by the authorities to purchase merinos in South Africa imported there originally from Europe; he brought back twenty-nine. A pioneer sheep breeder, Captain John MacArthur, visited England in 1803, and returned with half-a-dozen sheep from George III's flock of pure merinos. He endeavoured to interest the motherland in the prospects of Australia as a wool-producing country and carried with him specimens of wool; four years later the first

[1] In 1948 the percentages were respectively 97, 84, 87, 50.

consignment of wool was shipped to London from Botany Bay near Sydney, and the term botany thus came to be applied to fine wools.

The sheep industry in Australia expanded with astonishing rapidity. The cry went up: 'Put everything in four feet.' The sheep population, reinforced by importations direct from Europe, grew in four years (1789–93) from 29 to 526, in the next four years to 2,457, and in the next six years to 10,157. Then it soared: in the middle of the nineteenth century it numbered 17 millions, at the end of the century 70 millions, on the eve of the second world war 111 millions or one-seventh of the world's total number of sheep.[1] The predominant breed is the merino which formerly accounted for six-sevenths of her wool production (over one-half of the world's merino wool). In recent years, however, the quantity of crossbred wool has increased from one-seventh to two-sevenths. Australia has not only become the leading country in the size of her sheep population but her output of wool is on a scale of corresponding magnitude. A modest clip of 20,000 pounds in 1800 assumed the gigantic proportions of 500 million pounds a century later and over a thousand millions in our own day[2]—no less than one-fourth of the world supply. This prodigious expansion was due to an increase in the head of sheep as well as in the weight of the fleece. Exports kept pace with production since nearly the whole of the clip was shipped abroad: they constituted about two-fifths of total exports in values.[3]

The pre-eminence enjoyed by Australia in the world's pastoral industry may be attributed to a variety of reasons. One is the existence of vast plains not suited for intensive cultivation owing to low rainfall but well adapted for sheep-farming. Some sheep 'stations' are a great distance from the railroad and the wool is transported thither packed on the backs of camels and horses, in bullock and oxen carts, and in motor trucks. Another reason is the mild winters. The third

[1] In 1942 the peak of 125 m. was reached. Owing to drought the number fell in 1947 to 96 m. Early in 1951 it had recovered to nearly 116 m. (The high-water mark reached in the nineteenth century was 106 m. in 1891.)

[2] It averaged 995 m. lb. in 1934–38; 1,111 m. lb. in 1950.

[3] In 1938.

is the breeding of large sheep carrying a heavy fleece which, in the words of the Australian flockmaster, 'will fill the bale [of wool] and fatten the bank balance.' The fourth is the improved method of marketing—the efficiency with which the fleece is prepared for public auction by skirting and classing: important processes which were mentioned above. The careful attention to market requirements owes much to the influence of the brokerage houses which handle the wool at the selling end, and also to official encouragement of research and technical institutions for training experts. Lastly Australia benefited in the great era of expansion—the nineteenth century—by the low (virtually nominal) rents for leased land used as sheep runs, by light taxation, and by the cheap labour of the aborigines.

Australia leads the world in the production of wool: she is surpassed by New Zealand in the production of mutton. A handful of sheep were brought to New Zealand by Captain Cook. They died; and 'my hopes of stocking this country with a breed of sheep were blasted in a moment.' Then in the nineteenth century merinos were introduced from New South Wales, and they survived to become the nucleus of flourishing flocks which eventually exceeded 30 millions.[1] In the eighties occurred a dramatic transformation when the experiment of shipping frozen mutton proved successful. New Zealand, hitherto concerned only with growing wool, gave herself up to raising sheep primarily for the sake of the flesh; and accordingly she imported English breeds of long wool to cross with merinos. The product was the crossbred, a large sheep with an improved carcass though the wool is medium in quality. Crossbreds—the outstanding example is the Corriedale—have completely eclipsed merinos which furnished 90 per cent. of the total clip in 1882 and 2 per cent. fifty years later. The output of wool has quintupled in the past two generations.[2] Exports constituted one-fifth of total exports in values.[3]

Argentina has followed in the footsteps of New Zealand in giving precedence to the requirements of an expanding meat market abroad. In contrast with New Zealand, however, her

[1] 1939—32 m.; 1950—34 m.
[2] 1880—69 m. lb.; 1950—390 m. lb. (In 1934-38 it averaged 300 m. lb.)
[3] In 1938.

D

farmers are concerned not with mutton but with beef (as well as with cereals); hence her sheep population has registered a momentous decrease. In the nineties she had eighty million sheep; a quarter of a century later the number had been halved and it has not since shown any significant advance.[1] Investigators are convinced that 'sheep-breeding in Argentina is now on the decline;' sheep are being driven out to make room for immigrants; extensive pastoral ranches are being split up into farms; and grassland is being laid down to tillage and ploughed up by settlers on the soil. Wool production has also tended to diminish[2] though not to a corresponding extent because of the increased weight of the fleece. Argentina still ranks high among wool-producing and wool-exporting countries. Nevertheless the trend in her national economy is clearly evinced in the fact that exports constituted only one-tenth[3] (and sometimes even less) of total exports in values. Another South American state Uruguay, with a sheep population of about twenty millions, has not displayed the same tendency to abandon sheep-farming. It is believed that she must remain 'pre-eminently a land of native grasses' interspersed with cultivated land. Wool production, in marked contrast with Argentina, has nearly doubled since the beginning of the present century;[4] and exports constituted nearly half of total exports in values.[5] Both countries share a preference for crossbreds. Merinos were introduced early in the nineteenth century and crossed with native sheep and subsequently with English breeds. The proportion of merino wool in the total clip of these two countries within recent years has fluctuated between a sixth and an eighth. Altogether Argentina and Uruguay produce about nine-tenths of South American wool.[6]

The fourth great wool-producing region of the southern hemisphere, the Union of South Africa, falls into line with Australia in establishing the supremacy of the merino breed

[1] 1939—46 m.; 1950—47 m.
[2] 1900—440 m. lb.; 1950—415 m. lb.
[3] In 1938.
[4] 1900—88 m. lb.; 1950—163 m. lb. The number of sheep rose to nearly 23 m. in 1950.
[5] In 1938.
[6] Wool is also produced in the Falkland Islands.

which furnishes nine-tenths or more of the clip—some of it exhibiting very fine quality. The early Dutch colonists who settled in the Cape in the seventeenth century found a native stock, the so-called 'fat-tailed' sheep, non-woolled hairy animals useful only for mutton; much later merinos were brought from Europe. For two centuries the sheep industry languished. Its backward condition was apparently due in part to the trekking of Boer farmers northwards, and in part to inbreeding of flocks on secluded sheep runs which caused deterioration of the fleece in quality and quantity. Progress became rapid in the present century; the number of sheep was quadrupled in the first three decades, and in spite of a subsequent decline it remained over three times as high.[1] Wool production soared from a million pounds a hundred years ago to over 300 millions in recent times.[2] Exports did not lag behind; they constituted one-third of total exports in values.[3] The potentialities of the sheep industry in South Africa have not yet reached their limit; and in this respect she affords apparently an exception to the general trend.

The United States occupies a position exactly half-way between countries predominantly merino and those predominantly crossbred, for 50 per cent. of her sheep fall into each category. The opening decades of the nineteenth century witnessed the introduction of merinos, which in the west have continued a famous practice of their forebears—the annual migration from summer to winter pastures involving a trek of one to three hundred miles. At first sheep husbandry was located in the eastern states, but in the forties it invaded the middle west where wool could be produced more cheaply, and in the seventies it reached the far west. Broadly speaking merinos are the dominant type in the west, while in the east they have been crossed with English 'mutton' breeds in order to improve the flesh. The distinction between east and west corresponds to another distinction between 'farm states' and

---

[1] In 1904—12 m.; 1931—50 m.; 1939—39 m. These totals included about 5 m. non-woolled. (In 1950 the total was 32 m.)

[2] 1929—309 m. lb.; but in 1934–38 it averaged 261 m. lb. and in 1950 it was only 225 m. lb.

[3] In 1938.

'range states.' In the former conditions resemble those which prevail in England. Flocks are generally small, they are part of a mixed economy, and their function is to fertilize the soil on which crops are raised and to produce market lambs: wool is secondary. In the latter where two-thirds of the wool (called range or territorial wool) are grown the flocks are large, and they pasture on land which is not cultivated and is thrown open to free grazing. The number of sheep increased between the two world wars by a third and the total exceeded 50 millions; then it registered a decline of over a third.[1] Domestic wool production, which had reached 450 million pounds, fell almost proportionately. The United States thus takes rank as one of the great wool-producing countries of the world but in a vital respect she is exceptional: in marked contrast with her raw cotton she has virtually[2] no markets abroad for her raw wool which is consumed in her own mills.

The United States, like England, is not only a large producer of wool; she is also a large importer. On the eve of the second world war her imports were mainly the 'carpet' qualities; she no longer drew from other countries, to the same extent as formerly, the wool used for apparel fabrics—the latter being chiefly home-grown. Since 1939 wool consumption has risen considerably and the increase is reflected in the scale of her imports,[3] especially wool of apparel quality now greatly in excess of the native clip. In turn England, Argentina and Australia have held the leading position among the sources laid under contribution. Although the United States is dependent upon external supplies owing to the inadequacy of the domestic output for her manufacturing needs, she has pursued a policy towards imports which is in marked contrast with England's policy for over a hundred years. The cost of wool production is higher in the United States than elsewhere; and in response to the demand of the farmers for protection foreign wool came to be burdened with duties. The first tariff was levied

[1] 1939—51 m.; 1947—38 m.; 1950—30 m. Domestic wool production (which averaged 451 m. lb. in 1934-38) fell in 1950 to 264 m. lb.
[2] She exported 0·3 m. lb. in pre-war years, and 6·7 m. lb. in 1950.
[3] Imports were in 1939—242 m. lb.; in 1950—686 m. lb. Hence her dominating position in the post-war world market as the largest consumer of wool.

in 1816 and it has been repeatedly changed in the course of nearly a century and a half. In an effort to harmonize their conflicting interests a convention of growers and manufacturers was held after the Civil War in 1865 at Syracuse, where the following resolutions were framed: 'The woollen industry is especially commended for developing the agricultural and mechanical resources of the nation. The mutuality of the interests of the wool producers and wool manufacturers of the United States is established by the closest of commercial bonds, that of demand and supply. As the two branches involve largely the labour of the country [they should be given] equal protection [against] the accumulated capital and low wages of other countries. [Each should be developed], thus furnishing markets at home for the products of both interests.' Notwithstanding, the breach proved too strong to be bridged by paper resolutions; the duty imposed in 1867 exceeded 50 per cent. of the value of the imported wool; it was detrimental to the manufacturers, and dissensions between them and the growers soon revived. An English writer had remarked in the eighteenth century: 'The landed and trading interests are eternally jarring and jealous of each other's advantages.' A similar situation was reproduced in the United States between the producers and consumers of raw wool.

Finally a word may be added on two countries which figure prominently in the manufacture of wool textiles. In France before the French Revolution merino sheep were settled on an experimental government farm at Rambouillet, which has given its name to a famous breed. On the eve of the second world war France had ten million sheep; nevertheless she has not escaped the modern trend of giving precedence to mutton over wool. Her own domestic production was insufficient for her industrial needs and she became an importer on a considerable scale. Japan is in an exceptional position because she developed into an important manufacturing country, although she has to rely on foreign sources for almost all the wool consumed in her factories since domestic production is negligible. Her imports, drawn preponderately from Australia, multiplied twenty-five times between the two world wars.[1]

[1] They averaged before the first world war 10 m. lb.: in 1935—244 m. lb.

PART II
WOOL MANUFACTURES

CHAPTER FOUR

Early History

THE ARTS OF spinning and weaving rank among the most primitive of the industrial arts.[1] The fancy of a later age ascribed their origin to our primeval parents. 'Drapery is unquestionably so ancient as to have the honour of being the immediate successor of the fig-leaves. And though we are not quite certain that our great first father began it within his fair Eden, yet we are assured that Eve's spinistry and Adam's spade set to work together.' The tradition of the weavers connected them with Naamah:

> That Naamah, sister was to Tubal Cain,
> First us'd this Art, the Scripture doth make plain.

The history of the woollen and worsted industries in mediaeval and modern Europe starts with two great manufacturing seats—the Low· Countries and Florence. Flanders exported cloth to Italy during the Roman occupation; in the twelfth century it became, together with Brabant, a land of weavers and fullers—the industry reaching its peak in the early part of the fourteenth century. The superiority of the fabrics woven on Flemish looms is reflected in the appeal of the Oxford Parliament (1258) to the English nation 'not to seek over-precious garments' imported from abroad in place of native manufactures. The cloths of Flanders and Brabant were also bought by Florence in the rough state, and they were finished by the famous gild of cloth-finishers, *arte di calimala*. Another Florentine gild, *arte della lana*, comprised the clothmakers. Industry on the Continent was organized on the lines of the domestic system in England. The material was given out

---

[1] There are Biblical references to spinning, weaving, fulling and dyeing. 'The virtuous woman seeketh wool and flax. She layeth her hands to the spindle and her hands hold the distaff.' 'My days are swifter than a weaver's shuttle.' 'And the staff of his spear was like a weaver's beam.' 'The highway of the Fuller's Field.' 'Cloth of scarlet.'

to wage-earners who delivered the manufactured product. In the Low Countries these wage-earners earned the contemptuous soubriquet of 'blue nails,' and their relations with their capitalist employers were marred by great acrimony; we already hear of strikes in the first half of the thirteenth century.

Both the Low Countries and Florence alike were dependent on imported wool, mainly English, and this proved a primary cause of their swift decline. England grew conscious of the fact that she excelled in the quality of her wool which was indispensable to other countries, and she set to work to build up an industry of her own which would absorb the native supply. The success which attended her efforts is strikingly exhibited in the fate which overtook her competitors, even though they had recourse to Spanish wool in lieu of English wool. England wrested the lead in the weaving craft; and especially the towns of Flanders, once a workshop of the mediaeval world, found themselves eclipsed. Bruges, which in the thirteenth century claimed many thousands of looms, was sorely pressed and failed to maintain its former prosperity. Ypres with a population in 1408 of over eighty thousand inhabitants and three to four thousand cloth-workers—a substantial figure for a mediaeval town—had sunk in 1486 to less than six thousand inhabitants and barely a score or two cloth factories. Repeated attempts were made to exclude English cloth from the Low Countries: notwithstanding at the end of the middle ages the greatest wool producer in Europe was firmly established as also the greatest wool manufacturer. The romance of trade records few achievements more astonishing than this industrial revolution of the fifteenth century, in which England outstripped her formidable rivals and found a market for her cloth in every known quarter of the globe—obtaining control of her own market and ousting her competitors from the markets of other countries. The story of this achievement will be traced in the following pages.

For seven hundred years the English woollen and worsted industries were pre-eminently the staple manufacture of the realm. The prestige which they enjoyed down to the 'Industrial Revolution,' when they were surpassed in importance by the cotton industry, is reflected in the encomium bestowed upon them. A fifteenth-century Parliament declared that 'the making of cloth within all parts of the realm is the greatest occupation and living of the poor commons of this land.' In the seventeenth century the antiquary Camden described English cloth as 'one of the pillars of the state;' Chief Justice Coke termed it 'the worthiest and richest commodity of this kingdom;' Bacon called it 'this great wheel' of the realm; and the Venetian ambassador wrote home in 1610 that it formed 'the chief wealth of this nation.' A writer during the Civil War asserted that 'the most substantial and staple commodity that our country affords for the maintenance of trade is cloth,' and he explained the origin of the Woolsack as intended 'to put our judges in the House of Lords in mind of preserving and advancing the trade and manufactory of wool.' A petition of the House of Commons at the Restoration pronounced wool textiles to be 'the principal foundation upon which the foreign commerce of this kingdom moveth.' An act of parliament after the Revolution extolled them as 'the greatest and most profitable commodity of this kingdom on which the value of lands and the trade of the nation do chiefly depend.' The volume of eulogy continued in the following century with unabated force. In praising 'the richest and most valuable manufacture in the world,' Daniel Defoe wrote (1724): 'Nothing can answer all the ends of dress but good English broadcloth, fine camlets, druggets, serges and such like. These [other countries] must have, and with these none but England can supply them. Be their country hot or cold, torrid or frigid, 'tis the same thing, near the Equinox or near the Pole, the English woollen manufacture clothes them all; here it covers them warm from the freezing breath of the northern bear, and there it shades them and keeps them cool from the searching beams of a perpendicular sun. Let no man wonder that the woollen manufacture is arrived to such a magnitude when in a word it may be said to clothe the world.' Even as late as 1782 a writer is found to protest against the cotton mills 'lately erected in the neighbourhood of Manchester,' and to utter the warning that if these mills were 'suffered to destroy our woollen and stuff [worsted] manufactures they

will prove the most fatal discoveries ever made in Old
England.'

Among the industries of England the making of cloth has
several claims to its pre-eminence. Firstly, it was the premier
English industry from the twelfth to the nineteenth century.
To quote a petition laid before Parliament in 1800, it was
'our earliest, most extensive and most valuable manufacture.'
'There are many more people employed,' said a writer in
1683, 'and more profit made and money imported by this
manufactory [of cloth] alone than by all the other manufactories of England joined together.' A parliamentary report on
trade drawn up in the reign of William III estimated that after
the Restoration woollen goods accounted for 'near two-thirds'
of the general exports. 'The English through all the world,'
wrote a correspondent in 1672, 'are counted the most ingenious
in cloth.' It was, therefore, justly described as 'the master-wheel
of trade;' and Englishmen proudly boasted that we clothed
'half of Europe by our English cloth,' making the Continent
almost England's 'servant' since it wore England's 'livery.' Its
place in the national economy is also indicated by the compu-
tation which statisticians made near the end of the seventeenth
century that the annual value of wool textiles was nearly as
high as that of arable produce and higher than the rent of
agricultural land.

Secondly, the raw material was mainly raised at home—the
import of foreign wool being inconsiderable until the nineteenth
century—and native wool was generally reputed to be the
best in Europe. The mutual dependence of industry and
tillage inspired the prayer of the historian Fuller that 'the
plough may go along and the wheel around so that being fed
by the one and clothed by the other there may be, by God's
blessing, no danger of starvation in our nation;' but his vision
of an ordered commonwealth, in which the manufacturer and
the farmer co-operated harmoniously, was not fulfilled. The
English makers of cloth enjoyed untold advantage over their
competitors abroad in their ability to draw freely upon domestic sources for their raw material, but when they sought to
exclude alien buyers from the English wool market they came

into sharp collision with the English graziers. Thus the fortunes of the woollen manufacture were closely interwoven with those of agriculture, and the rivalry of these two great industries fills an important chapter in English economic history. In the nineteenth century the conflict between the landed and commercial interests was fought out over the question of cheap food; in the seventeenth and eighteenth centuries the conflict was over cheap raw materials. The prohibition of the export of native wool coupled with the unrestricted import of foreign wool—these were the cardinal problems of economic controversy debated in innumerable pamphlets and broadsheets. Even more fundamental was the fact that the progress of the textile industry seemed to divert the national energies from tillage into other and more unstable channels—a trend viewed with apprehension by those early economists who preferred to see the prosperity of England broad-based on land rather than on the shifting foundations of industry. 'We have too great a clothing commonwealth,' said a member of parliament in 1614; and Thomas Mun in *England's Treasure by Forraign Trade* voiced the general uneasiness when he wrote: Clothing 'is the greatest wealth and best employment of the poor of this kingdom, yet nevertheless we may peradventure employ ourselves with better safety, plenty and profit in using more tillage and fishing than to trust so wholly to the making of cloth; for in times of war or by other occasions, if some foreign princes should prohibit the use thereof in their dominions, it might suddenly cause much poverty and dangerous uproars especially by our poor people when they should be deprived of their ordinary maintenance.'

Thirdly, the cloth manufacture passed through every stage of industrial organization: thus its history illustrates with peculiar clearness the different phases of English industrial development. No other industry affords better material for studying the growth and decay of the various economic organisms which have taken root in English soil at one period or another—the gild system where the worker owns both the instruments of production and the raw material; the domestic system where he owns the instruments but not the material;

and the factory system where he owns neither the instruments nor the material.

Fourthly, wool textiles were the first industry to be subjected to national control and uniform regulation. The favourite child of the legislature, they were hedged round on every side with innumerable statutes 'by way of guards and fences.' As Adam Smith remarked: 'Our woollen manufacturers have been more successful than any other class of workmen in persuading the legislature that the prosperity of the nation depends upon the success and extension of their particular business.' Towards the end of the eighteenth century an abstract was published of 'laws relating to the growers of wool and to the manufacturers of, and dealers in, all sorts of woollen commodities.' It contained the titles of over three hundred laws then on the statute book. These laws regulated the clipping of sheep, the packing of wool, the length, breadth, weight and 'true making' of cloth, the use of materials in dyeing, the methods of fulling and 'tentering,' and the nature of the instruments for rowing and shearing. It is not surprising, then, to find a commission reporting as early as 1622 that 'the laws now in force concerning the making and dressing of cloth are so many and by the multitude of them are so intricate that it is very hard to resolve what the law is.' Not only did the government create for the protection of the textile industry an elaborate code of restrictive legislation which survived from the middle ages to the nineteenth century, but its foreign policy—and especially the encouragement of voyages of discovery—was largely inspired by the desire to open up new markets abroad.

Fifthly, cloth-making was the most widespread of all English industries. Although certain parts of the realm were preeminently the 'manufacturing districts' of England, there was probably not a town, village or hamlet throughout the length and breadth of the country which was not associated at some time or other with the production of cloth. Spinning was a cottage employment everywhere carried on by women and children, nothing more being required than a spindle and distaff or wheel; and weaving, similarly, was a household occupation. It was the universal character of the industry which gave it peculiar significance, since in its development were bound up the national fortunes and the interests of every section of the community.

Finally, the social influence exerted by the textile arts is displayed in the extent to which the English language has been enriched by words and phrases connected in their origin with the manufacture of cloth. No industry has left more traces in popular literature[1] and on popular speech. Such phrases as 'dyed in the wool,' 'to spin a yarn,' 'the thread of a discourse,' 'weavers of long tales,' 'a web of sophistry,' 'unravelling a mystery,' 'tangled skein,' 'on tenterhooks,' betray at once their source. We still speak of 'fine-drawn' theories and 'home-spun' youths. Many personal names betoken the original occupation of some ancestor—for example, Dyer, Fuller, Lister, Tailor, Tucker, Walker, Weaver, and Webster; and local nomenclature has preserved names like 'Rack-closes,' 'East-Stretch,' 'Tucking-Mill Field,' which refer to fulling and tentering cloth. Moreover the close identification of women with spinning is reflected in the use of the word 'spinster' to denote an unmarried woman.

We find occasional references to spinning and weaving in this country even in very early times. In Roman Britain there is said to have been an 'imperial weaving manufactory' at Winchester. In Anglo-Saxon England the mother of King Alfred is represented as skilled in spinning wool; and the chronicler Fabyan tells us that Edward the Elder 'sette his sonnes to scole and his daughters he sette to woll werke, takyng example of Charlys the Conquestour.' It is even possible that English woollen fabrics were being exported to the Continent already in the eighth century, for our earliest commercial treaty—the famous letter of Charles the Great to Offa, king of Mercia (796)—contains this passage: 'Our subjects make request concerning the size of the cloaks, that you will have them made of the same pattern as used to come to us in old

---

[1] Shakespeare uses frequent metaphors taken from spinning and weaving. 'The web of our life is of a mingled yarn, good and ill together.' 'Life is a shuttle.' 'Their thread of life is spun.' 'Ill-weav'd ambition, how much art thou shrunk!'

times.' However the authentic history of the English wool textile industries properly begins after the Norman Conquest, when we find gilds of weavers established under Henry I in London, Winchester, Oxford, Lincoln and Huntingdon. This shows that an organized weaving craft was conducted in the twelfth century as a trade and not merely as a household occupation for domestic use. About the same time large quantities of woad were imported for purposes of dyeing. Not only was cloth manufactured for the home market in numerous parts of the country during the twelfth and thirteenth centuries but many local varieties were exported. The cloths of Stamford found a market at Venice as early as 1265, and they gained a European reputation since it was considered worth while to imitate them at Milan. Other varieties sent abroad comprised those of York, Beverley, Coggeshall, Colchester, Lincoln, Maldon and Sudbury. These finer English cloths were also bought for the king's wardrobe, and the purchases made on the royal behalf furnish information as to the relative values of the different fabrics. Thus in 1182 the sheriff of Lincolnshire purchased cloth at the rate of 6s. 8d. for an ell[1] of scarlet, 3s. for green say, 1s. 8d. for grey say, and 3s. for an ell of blanket—erroneously supposed to have been 'named after its first maker, Thomas Blanket,' who actually lived a century and a half later.

The first notable event in the progress of the cloth manufacture occurred in the year 1258, when the Oxford Parliament gave articulate expression to the growing desire of English rulers to foster the native industry. It prohibited the export of wool, and ordered that 'the wool of the country should be worked up in England and not sold to foreigners and that everyone should use woollen cloth made within the country.' Those who hankered after the more delicate fabrics woven in the looms of Flanders were bidden 'not to seek over-precious garments.' This measure, which foreshadowed a protective policy, does not seem to have been successful. The government found it impossible for any length of time to prevent the export of wool, for it was anxious on political grounds to keep on friendly terms with the Flemish people. In the middle ages

[1] An ell is 45 inches.

England was the enemy of France; and Flanders, which was the gate into France, could be a valuable ally—and a dangerous foe inasmuch as her coast confronted our own. Accordingly another scheme was set on foot. The attempt to starve out the competition of the Flemish manufacturers, by refusing to supply them with raw material, was bound to fail not only because it excited intense ill-feeling against us but because the Flemings endeavoured to secure supplies of wool from other countries. It appeared a better plan to meet the rivalry of Flanders by improving the quality of domestic production. In former times the basis of industrial life was not machinery but craftsmanship, and thus skilled labour was the most important asset in building up a mediaeval industry. Hence the only way in which a native cloth manufacture could be successfully fostered was by inducing foreign craftsmen to settle in the realm and impart their technical knowledge and skill to native artisans.

The design of introducing alien weavers into England was actually present to the minds of English rulers in the thirteenth century, though the project did not bear fruit until the fourteenth century when Edward III embarked upon the experiment which helped to transform the economic life of England. His reign was a great landmark in the history of English wool textiles, yet to understand his work aright we must bear in mind that Edward was not the founder of the industry. The art of weaving was well established here as far back as the twelfth century, and Edward's work was not to create a new manufacture but to revive an old one which was decaying. This was accomplished by bringing over Flemish weavers into England. There was great unrest in the Low Countries owing to various political and economic causes, and the Flemings therefore lent a ready ear to the solicitations of English agents who invited them to settle here. In 1331 Edward granted letters of protection to John Kempe of Flanders, 'weaver of woollen cloths,' and to 'the men, servants and apprentices' whom he brought with him to exercise his craft in England; at the same time similar letters were offered to all workers of cloth who came from over the sea to ply their trade or 'mistery' within the realm. In 1337 an act of parliament promised lavish favours

E

and 'fair treating' to alien settlers. 'All the cloth-workers of strange lands,' recited the act, 'of whatsoever country they be, which will come into England, Ireland, Wales and Scotland within the king's power shall come safely and surely and shall be in the king's protection and safe conduct to dwell in the same lands choosing where they will; and to the intent that the said cloth-workers shall have the greater will to come and dwell here, our sovereign lord the king will grant them franchises as many and such as may suffice them.' As a result of this invitation there was a large influx of alien weavers, dyers and fullers who came not only from Flanders but from Zeeland and Brabant. They took up their residence in the large towns— London, York, Winchester, Norwich, Bristol and Abingdon— and also scattered themselves over the countryside.

An old historian, the 'worthy' Fuller, describes the coming of the strangers in quaint and exaggerated terms. 'The king and state began now to grow sensible of the great gain the Netherlands got by our English wool; in memory whereof the duke of Burgundy not long after instituted the Order of the Golden Fleece—wherein indeed the fleece was ours, the golden theirs, so vast their emolument by the trade of clothing. Our king therefore resolved, if possible, to reduce the trade of his own country who as yet were ignorant of that art, as knowing no more what to do with their wool than the sheep that wear it (as to any artificial and curious drapery); their best clothes then being no better than friezes, such their coarseness for want of skill in the making. The intercourse now being great betwixt the English and the Netherlands unsuspected emissaries were employed by our king into those countries, who brought themselves into familiarity with those Dutchmen as were absolute masters of their trade but not masters of themselves, as either journeymen or apprentices. These bemoaned the slavishness of these poor servants whom their masters used rather like heathen than Christians, yea, rather like horses than men. Early up and late in bed and all day hard work and harder fare (a few herrings and mouldy cheese), and all to enrich the churls their masters without any profit to themselves. But how happy these should be if they would but come into England bringing their

mistery with them and which would provide them welcome in
all places. Here they should feed on beef and mutton. Happy
the yeoman's house into which one of these Dutchmen did
enter bringing industry and wealth along with them. Such who
came in strangers within their doors soon after went out bride-
grooms and returned sons-in-law, having married the daughters
of their landlords who first entertained them; yea, the yeomen
in whose houses they harboured soon proceeded gentlemen
gaining great worship to themselves, arms and worship to their
estates.' Fuller adds that the strangers were 'sprinkled everywhere,' giving as the reason the king's apprehension 'lest on
discontent they might embrace a general resolution to return.'
However welcome the immigrant weavers may have been in
country districts, their presence in towns was very distasteful to
their industrial competitors; for while they proved amenable
to the civic authorities, they refused to submit to the control of
the native weavers or enter their gild. The English artisans
resented the rivalry of the newcomers, who set at defiance their
monopoly and refused to contribute towards the annual dues
which the weavers' gilds owed the Crown. The king intervened
on behalf of the alien craftsmen and ordered that they should
not be compelled to join the weavers' gild; but the friction
between denizens and aliens did not die down, and even in the
fifteenth century the foreign weavers complained that they
were 'grievously persecuted and harassed' by the native
weavers.

The experiment of Edward III was attended with complete
success. The presence of foreign 'captains of industry' in this
country co-operated with other factors—the protective measures of the government and the natural forces of recovery and
expansion—to bring about an industrial revival which extended
even to districts where no alien settlement is recorded. Aided
by these combined influences, the English cloth-makers in the
words of an old writer (1613) grew so 'perfect in this mistery
that it is at this instant the glory of our traffic and maintenance
of our poor, many hundred thousands depending wholly on the
same, chief pillar to our prince's revenue, the life of our
merchant, the living of our clothier.' Not only did Edward

encourage the settlement of aliens, he also took steps to protect
the native industry from foreign competition and to ensure an
adequate supply of raw material. On the one hand he forbade
the import of manufactured cloth; on the other he prohibited
the export of home-grown wool. It is true that neither Edward
nor his successors adhered very strictly to a protectionist policy.
They were too deeply engrossed in foreign diplomacy to
pursue with any consistency a planned economy, and their
industrial projects were easily sacrificed to their political
ambitions and dreams of aggrandizement on the Continent.
One of the charges against the Lancastrian government was
that wool had 'course and passage out of the realm, wherefore
all strangers take but little reward to buy our English cloth but
make it themselves;' and the Yorkist dynasty sought to gain
popularity by reverting to a system of protection. Thus in the
middle ages the latter was only fitfully maintained, and we
have to wait until the seventeenth century for its definite
adoption.

When the measures of Edward III are taken in conjunction
with those of his predecessors, there seems no valid reason to
deny him the credit for an enlightened outlook consciously
inspired by the desire to stimulate the growth of a native cloth
manufacture. In any event they helped to prepare the day for
England's transformation from a land of agricultural labourers
into a land of industrial artisans. Even in his own lifetime his
measures were rewarded with surprising success. A proof of the
advance made during his reign is that woollen fabrics were
being exported in sufficient quantity to make it worth while to
impose customs duties upon them. In spite of their protests the
exporters of cloth had little ground for complaint in comparison
with the exporters of wool, for the latter paid a duty of 33 per
cent. and the former under 2 per cent. The second half of the
fourteenth century witnessed, indeed, a remarkable expansion
of the textile industry. In the space of fifty years the production
of broadcloth in England for sale was more than trebled and the
export of broadcloth was multiplied no less than ninefold.
Other statistics show how abundantly this growth was maintained—in the early decades of the sixteenth century the export

of broadcloth became twentyfold apart from the increase in kersies and worsteds. Moreover, while thirty thousand sacks of wool were sent abroad annually in the fourteenth century, the number had fallen to five thousand in the sixteenth century. These figures afford eloquent testimony to the progress of a revolution which was converting England into an industrial country, whose staple export was no longer raw wool but manufactured wool.

The second great landmark in the history of English wool textiles was the immigration of Dutch and Walloon weavers in the sixteenth century, just as the influx of Flemish weavers in the fourteenth century constitutes the first. The cruelty of Spanish rule in the Netherlands caused a large exodus of the most skilful and industrious section of the population. The exiles were welcomed by the English government both as religious refugees and as a valuable accession to the economic resources of the country, since they established a new branch of wool textiles. This was the manufacture of the finer fabrics known as the new draperies, many of which were either unknown here or were beyond the technical skill of native workers. A very curious list is given: 'bays, arras, says, tapestry, mokadoes, staments, carsays and other outlandish commodities.'[1] 'It surpasseth my skill,' confessed Fuller, 'to name the several stuffs' made of worsted. He added: 'The nimble woof, its artificial dancing in several postures about the standing warp, produceth infinite varieties in this kind.' An old English rhyme ran:

> Hops, Reformation, *Bays*, and Beer
> Came into England all in a year.

The strangers settled in a number of towns—Norwich whose prosperity now increased by leaps and bounds, London, Canterbury, Colchester, Rye, Sandwich, Southampton, Stamford and Yarmouth. In spite of the benefits arising from their

---

[1] *Bays:* originally a cloth of fine and light texture. *Arras:* a rich tapestry fabric. *Says:* a cloth of fine texture resembling serge (a mixture of worsted and woollen). *Mokadoes:* a kind of cloth. *Staments:* a coarse worsted. *Carsays:* an obsolete form of kersey, a narrow woollen cloth. These terms may not have always retained their original significance.

presence there was great difficulty in adjusting the relations between the aliens and the local inhabitants. The blind attachment of the native weavers to their own narrow interests, coupled with their jealousy of foreign competitors and their dislike of innovations, made them look with hostile eyes upon the introduction of the new draperies: 'slight and vain commodities,' as they termed them, 'wherein the common people delight.' In the course of time the refugees were absorbed into the mass of the population, and the national life was enriched and strengthened by the infusion of fresh blood. In recounting the various factors which have helped to build up the industrial supremacy of our country, we must not forget the debt of gratitude which England owes to the strangers within her gates, whose technical skill and knowledge of the industrial arts enabled her to wrest the secrets of the woollen manufacture from her rivals and become the workshop of the world.

CHAPTER FIVE

Organization

WE HAVE NOW to speak about the men and women who carded and combed and spun the wool, wove at the looms, and fulled and dressed and dyed the cloth.

The fundamental interest of the English woollen manufacture lies in the fact that it has passed through every stage of industrial organization: the gild system, the domestic system, and the factory system. In the order of historical sequence the gild system must be described first. Under the gild system, as we shall interpret it, the various classes of textile artisans owned both the material on which they worked and the instruments of production. They were independent craftsmen who sold not their labour but the product of their labour, a distinction of vital economic significance. Thus the spinners bought the wool and sold the yarn; the weavers bought the yarn and sold the cloth; the fullers bought the cloth raw and sold it fulled; the shearmen bought the cloth fulled and sold it dressed; the dyers bought either wool or cloth and sold it dyed. This form of organization was rudimentary, but it gave birth to the most remarkable institution of mediaeval industrial life—namely the craft gild.

The craft gild may be defined as a body of skilled workers, who dwelt as a rule within the walls of the same town and carried on the same occupation. It was essentially an urban institution adapted to the period extending from the twelfth to the sixteenth century when the manufacture of cloth was carried on mainly in towns. Here the different groups of weavers, fullers, shearmen and dyers were organized in gilds; and in their capacity as gildsmen they enjoyed various rights and were burdened with various obligations. The gild comprised three classes of members—the masters, the journeymen, and the apprentices. It was usually necessary to pass through all the three grades of membership: the apprentice became a journeyman, the journeyman rose to the status of a master. The length of apprenticeship varied but the period of seven years was generally recognized as the proper term in which the apprentice could acquire 'sufficient cunning.' Weavers as a rule were not allowed to receive apprentices under the age of fourteen, for a younger boy was not considered strong enough to work a loom. After completing his term of training the apprentice was free to become a journeyman or wage-earner, and seek employment as a hired workman. Usually he remained with his master for another year though he was now paid wages, yet every journeyman looked forward to the day when he would cease to be a journeyman and would take his place among the masters of the gild as a fully qualified craftsman. Two or three years at least necessarily elapsed before the journeyman was in a position to claim entry into the inner circle of the gild, and the interval afforded a breathing-space in which he could accumulate sufficient capital to set up in his own workshop. However capital played as a rule a subordinate part in mediaeval industry, and his tools and technical skill were the resources upon which the master craftsman was content to rely to gain a livelihood. His wooden loom could be made with his own hands, and he had no difficulty in obtaining a supply of wool on credit. In the early days of the woollen manufacture—and in the West Riding of Yorkshire down to the nineteenth century—no impassable gulf separated the master from the workman, and the masters themselves might be artisans recruited from the ranks of the labouring class.

The functions of the craft gilds were in the main fourfold: the control of industry, the performance of religious and social duties, the relief of the poor, and the maintenance of good relations between the gild brethren.

The industrial ordinances framed by the gild were designed to protect the consumer against defective wares and the producer against the competition of untrained workmen. The rules in force among the weavers of Bristol will serve as an illustration —they fixed the width of the cloth and directed that 'if the threads are deficient in the cloth or are too far apart, which the weavers called *tosed*, that cloth and the instrument on which it is worked ought to be burnt.' The same penalty was inflicted when the cloth was made of woollen thread called *thrums*,[1] or if it were 'worse in the middle than at the ends.' Nowadays a manufacturer may sell his cloth good or bad as he pleases, but the gild assumed responsibility for the work turned out by its members and the main task of the gild authorities was the inspection of workshops. Defective wares were confiscated and the maker was fined or placed in the pillory or even, as a last resource, expelled from the gild. In mediaeval times men conceived industry in the light of a public service carried on 'for the common profit' in the interests of the community as a whole; and the ordinances of the gilds repeatedly insisted that dishonest workmanship brought discredit upon the industry and those engaged in it. Anyone who suffered from the incompetency of a workman sought redress from the gild authorities. At Nottingham 'one Robert Mellers, bellfounder, at the feast of Christmas gave to William Nicholson a piece of white kersey to be fulled, sheared and scoured, and redelivered to the same Robert Mellers within three weeks then next following; in which piece of kersey a fault of workmanship was discovered; whereupon John Sainton and Robert Strelley, then being wardens and masters of the whole craft of fullers within the town of Nottingham, surveyed that fault and thereupon decided that the aforesaid William Nicholson should lose his whole work upon the aforesaid piece of kersey and should receive nothing for his labour.' In addition wages and prices were often regulated. Instead of allowing a master to pay wages and charge prices as he listed, many gilds fixed the remuneration of the artisan and determined the prices of commodities. Among the London shearmen, for example, whenever a master employed a stranger it was the duty of the gild authorities to 'see the "foreigner" work and conscientiously set his salary between his master and him and there to be bound four years in covenant.' Wages here depended upon the capacity of the wage-earner, and we also observe the long period of engagement. The gildsman who set the brethren at defiance was roughly handled. The dyers' gild at Coventry undertook to

[1] The unwoven ends of the warp.

work only at certain rates, and when a number of dyers refused to be bound by these rates the gild hired Welshmen and Irishmen to waylay and kill them. This drastic treatment of 'blacklegs' represented the mediaeval form of picketing.

In the middle ages religion played a very considerable part in the lives of the people. Every gild had a patron saint upon whose altars it was wont to maintain lights: the tutelary saint of the wool-combers was Bishop Blaize, the reputed founder of their craft, in whose honour processions were held even in the nineteenth century. In addition to the performance of their religious duties, the gilds exhibited plays and pageants as part of their contribution to the social life of the community. In these pageants were portrayed Biblical incidents—at Norwich, for instance, the Mercers, Drapers and Haberdashers presented the Creation of the World; the Shearmen, Fullers and Woollen Weavers depicted Abel and Cain; the Worsted Weavers the Holy Ghost.

In the capacity of friendly societies the gilds provided for the support of their poorer members. In old age or sickness the poverty-stricken brethren enjoyed an allowance from the common box, and gildsmen were expected to leave legacies for the purpose. Thus the weavers of Gloucester received a bequest of forty pounds to be distributed annually among the poor who were to return the loan at the end of the year. Money was also bequeathed to 'succour young men that were minded to cloth-making;' and philanthropists used their wealth to give a start in life to poor young men who were lent sums of money, often without interest. The most notable was Sir Thomas White, founder of St. John's College at Oxford, who owed his fortune to the cloth trade and perpetuated his memory in twenty-four towns by his endowments.

Another purpose of the gilds was to settle all disputes between their members, and no craftsman was permitted to sue a fellow-gildsman in a court of law without the leave of the gild authorities. The rule was intended to strengthen the feeling of solidarity among the brethren, to promote 'perfect love and charity' among those who were bound together by ties of social and economic interests. The same principle underlay the injunction that no one must seek an unfair advantage over his fellows; it was strictly forbidden to entice a servant away from his master or a customer from a dealer. The London shearmen even ordered that if one master had three journeymen and another had none, 'the wardens shall go to him that hath the said journeymen and shall take of them such as the goodman of the house may best forbear, and deliver him to him that hath none and hath need to have.'

Membership of the gilds was compulsory on the skilled operatives in an industry, and the obligations extended to women. The employment of women workers has always been a marked feature of the woollen manufacture. They served as wool-sorters and wool-packers, carders and spinners, weavers and dyers. One-fourth of the cloth woven in York at the end of the fourteenth century was the work of women; and they were enrolled as apprentices and admitted to the membership of the crafts. A large portion of the cloth made at Wakefield in 1396 was manufactured in 'Emma Earle's weaving sheds,' whilst among the pilgrims in Chaucer's *Prologue* was a 'wife of Bath' who made cloths:

> Of cloth-making she had such an haunt
> She passed them of Ypres and of Ghent.[1]

The wool-packers of Southampton, whose duty it was to pack the wool for transport, seem to have been entirely women and they afford a rare example of a women's industrial gild. They were organized as a company of woman artisans and were governed by two wardens elected by the women from their own ranks. Among their ordinances was the injunction that the members were 'not to bawle nor scold oon with anither.' As regards wool-sorting a statute of 1554 declared that 'the experience thereof consisteth only in women, as clothiers' wives and their women servants.' Women are found, in fact, in every branch of wool textiles. At the end of the sixteenth century one Rachel Thierry applied for the monopoly of pressing all serges made in Hampshire. The application was strongly resisted by the municipal authorities of Southampton who

---

[1] Haunt=use, practice. Passed=surpassed.

asserted that 'the woman Thierry is very poor and beggarly, idle, a prattling gossip unfit to undertake a matter of so great a charge. She is very untrustworthy and we should hold them worse than mad that would hazard or commit their goods into her hands. And to conclude: she is generally held amongst us an unfit woman to dwell in a well-governed commonwealth.' In the course of time an agitation sprang up against the employment of women workers. It was attacked in the fifteenth century on the ground that they competed with men, who were said to deserve the chief consideration since they did 'the king service in his wars and in the defence of this his land;' it was also alleged that women were 'not of sufficient power' to weave certain kinds of cloth. Weavers were forbidden, therefore, to employ women except those who were now getting their livelihood from weaving. As a rule a woman was allowed to exercise her husband's craft after his death and even employ journeymen and apprentices.

The second form of industrial organization opened up a new and momentous stage in economic evolution. This was the domestic system in which the material was owned, not by the workers themselves, but by a class of employers who united all branches of the manufacture under a single control. The master craftsman of the gild system, who combined trading and handicraft functions and disposed freely of his wares to consumers, yielded place to the small master of the domestic system who was confined to the purely manual functions and depended henceforth on an employer for the provision of materials. He was, in short, transformed into a wage-earner paid by the piece, although the work was still carried on at home (as under the gild system) and he was employed by more than one master. The domestic system must be distinguished from the factory system—the third form of industrial organization—since factory workers own neither the material as under the gild system, nor the instruments of production as under the domestic system; and they are assembled under an employer's roof, subjected to the discipline of the factory, and confined to the service of one master. The domestic system, however, resembled the factory system in one vital respect: it was organized on a capitalist basis, and the control of industry was vested in the hands of the employers of labour who stood (except in Yorkshire) outside the ranks of the manual craftsmen. In the gild system, on the other hand, the control of industry lay in the hands of the manual workers themselves who exercised it through the medium of an assembly, a council and their own elected officials.

It is a popular error to date capitalism from the era of the 'Industrial Revolution.' Capitalism existed in the woollen and worsted industries four centuries prior to the introduction of machinery, and there was a wage-earning class engaged in making cloth at least as early as the fourteenth century. The growth of capitalism in wool textiles depended primarily upon the operation of two factors: the extent of the market and the division of labour. A local market may easily be supplied by independent bodies of craftsmen, but a national or international market demands a more complex structure; again, where the division of labour is small, the possibilities of co-operation among the various classes of artisans are greater. The working of these two factors explains the evolution of the textile industry on capitalist lines. An ever-widening market and a corresponding increase in production called for an intricate organization and also made the investment of capital a profitable venture; while the variety of processes involved in the preparation and manufacture of cloth seemed to necessitate centralized control under an entrepreneur. Cloth passed through many hands; and it was thus inevitable that the combers, spinners, weavers, fullers, shearmen and dyers should become dependent upon the clothiers as the capitalist employers were termed. One writer asserts that 'from the wool grower to the consumer a piece of broadcloth passes through a hundred different hands, and there are near the same number of hands dependent on the woollen manufacturer though not actually concerned in it.' These figures seem rhetorical. A more sober estimate gives the number of persons employed on a single piece of cloth as fourteen; this includes the spinners, weavers, burlers, fullers and shearmen, but not wool growers, dyers, makers of looms and

spinning wheels, transport workers, and others connected
directly or indirectly with the cloth trade. Without attempting
any precise calculations it is enough to state that the division of
labour was considerable. Now it is manifest that the best
results in any industry are attained where the different bodies
of artisans engaged in it are brought to devote themselves to
particular processes under the guidance of a controlling
authority. Division of labour is the indispensable basis of
economic progress, for technical perfection is only achieved by
concentration on details—doing one thing at a time and doing
it well. The author of *Considerations on the East India Trade* (1701)
anticipated Adam Smith in the stress which he laid upon the
importance of the division of labour: 'The more variety of
artists to every manufacture the less is left to the skill of single
persons; the greater the order and regularity of every work the
same must needs be done in less time, the labour must be less,
and consequently the price of labour less though wages should
not be abated. Thus a piece of cloth is made by many artists;
one cards and spins, another makes the loom, another weaves,
another dyes, another dresses the cloth; and thus to proper
artists proper parts of the work are still assigned; the weaver
must needs be more skilful and expeditious at weaving if that
shall be his constant and whole employment, than if the same
weaver is also to card and spin and make the loom and weave
and dress and dye the cloth. So the spinner, the fuller, the dyer
or cloth-worker must needs be more skilful and expeditious at
his proper business which shall be his whole and constant
employment, than any man can be at the same work whose
skill shall be puzzled and confounded with variety of other
business.' The parliamentary committee which framed the
famous *Report on the State of the Woollen Manufacture of England*
(1806) attributed 'the acknowledged excellence, and till of late
superiority, of the cloths of the west of England' to the great
skill which each class of workmen in the west country acquired
in keeping to its 'proper line' and performing its own particular
operations.

The domestic system assumed different forms in the west

and in the north of England. We shall examine first the structure of industrial society in the west country.

In the foreground of the picture stands the capitalist (clothier). He was the pivot of the textile industry and in his hands was concentrated the whole control. One writer even compared him with the sun inasmuch as 'he scattered life and its supports to everyone around him.' Another described his occupation as one of 'surpassing charity, for clothing not only our own nation but foreign countries and above all getting so many poor folks on work in carding, spinning and such like hand-maids of their trade, as they surmount those who relieve beggars at their gates.' The position of the clothier at the very centre of the cloth trade enabled him to supervise and direct every stage of production. He was responsible, in fact, for the whole series of processes from the time when the wool was picked, washed, carded and spun, until it was woven, fulled and 'perfected' into cloth.[1]

What were the functions of the clothier? The west country clothier (unlike the Yorkshire clothier) was not a manufacturer in the literal sense in which the word was used before the 'Industrial Revolution'—namely, a man who works with his own hands. The actual manufacturers were the weavers and other operatives, while the clothiers assumed the functions of the entrepreneur—that is, they directed the industry and left to others the execution of its details. Most clothiers probably never learnt the regular trade of a weaver; indeed, we find men entering the occupation late in life after essaying other callings. The west country clothier was in short an employer not a manual worker. Nor was he a manufacturer in the modern sense. The modern manufacturer is first and foremost an indus-trial capitalist. He carries on the industry under his own roof, and makes it his function to study and perfect in detail the whole business of production. The clothier was a trading rather than an industrial capitalist; he was primarily concerned

[1] The clothier, although the most important, was not the only capitalist employer in the woollen industry. There was a class of market spinners, who 'set many spinners on work' and sold the yarn without working it up into cloth. Similarly in the worsted industry there was a class of master wool-combers, who owned wool and employed combers and spinners to convert it into thread, which they after-wards sold.

with buying and selling; he bought the raw material and he sold the finished product; the actual details of cloth-making were left to spinners, weavers and shearmen. Whether the weaver did the task himself or employed assistants, whether he used one kind of loom or another, did not matter to the clothier. He did not go round the weavers' homes and see how the work was being done; he examined the work only when it was brought back. However we cannot describe the clothier as merely a merchant whose province was nothing more than the sale of goods, for he was also an employer of the various groups of artisans who handled his material. In brief we must avoid the use of modern terms and modern analogies.

The advent of a capitalist class of clothiers can be traced as remotely as the fourteenth century, and it developed in import- ance as the middle ages drew to a close. The 'captains of industry' whom Edward III invited to England were clearly not simple artisans but capitalists. John Kempe took with him from Flanders 'men, servants and apprentices;' and 'the workers of wools and cloths'. who came from other parts had their 'men and their servants.' At Bristol we even get glimpses of the beginnings of a factory system. Thomas Blanket, after- wards bailiff of the town, and other burgesses set up looms for weaving cloth and employed in their own establishments 'weavers and other workmen.' This was in the year 1339, though the attempt to concentrate hired workmen under one roof was doubtless exceptional at this early period. In the closing years of the fourteenth century the large manufacturers were apparently restricted to a few centres, but the rapid extension of the woollen manufacture soon brought in its wake a growing body of capitalist employers. They originated in various ways. Some were probably dealers in wool who caused the raw material to be worked up into cloth and then disposed of it in the market. Others were shearmen who employed work- men in all the earlier processes of carding, spinning, weaving, fulling and dyeing. Others were recruited from artisans engaged in the subordinate branches, such as weavers, fullers and dyers. As a rule the clothiers must have been men of substantial position in command of capital. It is apparent that the business which they conducted was not considered to involve social inferiority, for we read of a mayor of Canterbury who 'took upon him the occupation of making of cloths and lived like a gentleman;' and in the west country the clothier was called the 'gentleman clothier.'

The extent to which textile workers had become dependent upon an employer was signally shown in 1525 when Cardinal Wolsey endeavoured to raise war taxes. The clothiers of Suffolk, under pressure from the minister, submitted to the imposition but were left without money to pay the wages of their workfolk. They were forced to dismiss their carders and spinners, weavers and fullers, and a revolt against the government was only narrowly averted. The story is told in Holinshed: 'The duke of Suffolk, sitting in commission about the subsidy in Suffolk, persuaded by courteous means the rich clothiers to assent thereto; but when they came home and went about to discharge and put from them their spinners, carders, fullers, weavers and other artificers which they kept in work aforetime, the people began to assemble in companies.' The incident serves, in part at any rate, to explain why the Tudor monarchy disliked the development of the capitalist system. Upon the discretion and foresight of a limited group of men had now come to depend the welfare and even the existence of the great body of the industrial population.

Many rich clothiers worked their way up in life from very small beginnings. One of the leading clothiers of the sixteenth century was Peter Blundell who deserves to rank as one of the 'Worthies of Devon.' He was born at Tiverton in the year 1520, and his parents were so poor that as a boy 'he was obliged to run on errands and do other little services for the common carriers' in order to support himself. As he grew older he tended their horses, and the fidelity with which he performed his duties gained him the goodwill of his employers. 'With much care he saved a little money, bought a piece of kersey cloth and sent it to London by one of the carriers who charged him nothing for the carriage, sold it to great advantage, and made him a faithful return. The profits from this kersey and other savings enabled him to purchase others which he sent and sold

F

in like manner.' In a short time he was able to buy 'as many kersies as would load one horse with which he went himself to London, where he was employed some time by the agents in the kersey trade.' He remained in London till he had acquired wealth sufficient to start his own manufacture of kersies, when he returned to Tiverton and established a business. He built up a large enterprise; and when he died, eighty-one years old, he left a fortune of £40,000 which then represented an immense amount. A great part of his fortune was devoted to charitable bequests. He remembered the saying of William of Wykeham who founded a school at Winchester and a college at Oxford in the fourteenth century—'Though I am not myself a scholar, I will be the means of making more scholars than any scholar in England'—and in emulation of his renowned predecessor he founded the Free Grammar School which Defoe a century later praised as 'the beauty of Tiverton.'

The most famous clothier of the sixteenth century was John Winchcombe familiarly known as Jack of Newbury, whom Fuller acclaimed as 'the most considerable clothier (without fancy and fiction) England ever beheld.' Many legends have gathered round his name yet he was undoubtedly an historical figure. His will is still preserved in which he bequeathed forty pounds to Newbury parish church and legacies to his servants, and his epitaph is shown in Newbury church of which he built the tower. In the *Journal to Stella* the author of *Gulliver's Travels* describes a visit to the notable St. John, afterwards Lord Bolingbroke, who had married one of Winchcombe's descendants. 'His lady is descended from Jack Newbury of whom books and ballads are written; and there is an old picture of him in the house.' In *The Pleasant History of John Winchcombe* the prosperity of the great clothier is depicted by Thomas Deloney in glowing terms:

> Within one room being large and long
> There stood two hundred Looms full strong.
> Two hundred men the truth is so
> Wrought in these Looms all in a row.
> By every one a pretty boy

Sate making quills with mickle joy.
And in another place hard by
An hundred women merrily
Were carding hard with joyful cheer
Who singing sate with voices clear.
And in a chamber close beside
Two hundred maidens did abide
In petticoats of Stammell red
And milk-white kerchers on their head.
These pretty maids did never lin [cease work]
But in that place all day did spin.
Then to another room came they
Where children were in poor array
And everyone sate picking wool
The finest from the coarse to cull.
Within another place likewise
Full fifty proper men he spies
And these were Shearmen everyone
Whose skill and cunning there was shown.
And hard by them there did remain
Full fourscore Rowers taking pain.
A Dye-house likewise had he then
Wherein he kept full forty men.
And likewise in his Fulling Mill
Full twenty persons kept he still.

The reputation which his cloth obtained may be gauged from the advice of the English envoy at Antwerp to the Protector Somerset to send over 'a thousand of Winchcombe's kersies' in discharge of a debt. Even at the end of the seventeenth century Jack of Newbury was the chief figure in the pageant of the cloth-workers of London.

John Winchcombe was not the only clothier in the sixteenth century who set up a manufactory and gathered servants and looms under one roof. It is probable that the agrarian changes, which turned vast numbers of labourers adrift from the soil, furnished the recruits whom clothiers with some capital at their command were able to utilize. The monasteries were occasionally converted into factories. Thus William Stumpe, a clothier of Malmesbury, rented Osney Abbey in 1546 and undertook to employ as many as two thousand workmen who were to labour 'continually in cloth-making for the succour of the city of Oxford.' Stumpe had also taken over Malmesbury Abbey; and Leland, the antiquary, gives the following description. 'The whole lodgings of the Abbey be now longing to one Stumpe, an exceeding rich clothier that bought them of the king. At this present time every corner of the vast houses of office that belonged to the Abbey be full of looms to weave cloth in. There be made now every year in the town three thousand cloths.' Another clothier, who sought to obtain possession of the Abbey of Abingdon, was Tuckar a cloth-maker of Burford. One of Thomas Cromwell's agents wrote to his master in 1538 that the town of Abingdon was likely to decay unless the people were set to work to 'drape cloth.' Tuckar had promised that he would expend a hundred marks a week in wages to cloth-makers of the town during his life on condition that he was allowed to rent the lands and fulling mills of the Abbey. 'He is a just man both in word and deed, and *daily employs five hundred of the king's subjects*. If he had carding and spinning he would employ many more. With Cromwell's favour he would set the inhabitants of Abingdon to work, if they will work, so that they would gain more wages in a few years coming than in twenty years past. Weekly need constrains him to send to Abingdon his cart laden with wool to be carded and spun, and likewise he sends to Stroudwater [Gloucestershire].' Thomas Cromwell was doubtless well disposed towards the woollen industry; his father was a fuller and shearman, he himself was married to the daughter of a shearman, and at one time he even carried on the business of finishing cloths.

Other famous clothiers were the Springs of Lavenham, the Tames of Fairford and Thomas Dolman of Newbury. When Dolman gave up cloth-making the weavers of Newbury lamented:

> Lord have mercy upon us miserable sinners,
> Thomas Dolman has built a new house and
> turned away all his spinners.

Thomas Spring, surnamed the rich clothier, bequeathed £200 to finish Lavenham steeple and money for a thousand masses—he died on the eve of the Reformation—and his daughter married a son of the earl of Oxford. John Tame, who lived in the reign of Edward IV, built up a large cloth manufacture at Cirencester and kept vast flocks of sheep at Fairford, prospering so well that he became owner of several landed estates. His son, Edmund Tame, received a visit from Henry VIII by whom he was knighted; he became lord of the manor of Fairford and was three times high sheriff of Gloucestershire. Fairford, observes Leland, 'never flourished before the coming of the Tames unto it.' His remarks on Bath are worth quoting to show the influence which the clothiers were exercising upon the destinies of the towns in which they were established. 'The town hath of a long time since been continually most maintained by making of cloth. There were [within living memory] three clothiers at one time thus named, Style, Kent and Chapman, by whom the town of Bath then flourished. Since the death of them it hath somewhat decayed.' Lastly we may mention three big clothiers who lived in the north country early in the sixteenth century—Cuthbert of Kendal, Hodgkins of Halifax and Martin Brian of Manchester—each of whom kept 'a great number of servants at work, spinners, carders, weavers, fullers, dyers and shearmen, etc. to the great admiration of all that came into their houses to behold them.'

The movement towards a factory system, already foreshadowed in the career of Thomas Blanket, was frowned upon by the Tudor monarchy which was uneasy at the opportunity it seemed to afford for unruly spirits to collect together in one place and stir up rioting and disorder. Hence the Weavers' Act of Philip and Mary (1555) recited that 'the weavers of this realm have complained that the rich and wealthy clothiers do in many ways oppress them; some by setting up and keeping in their houses diverse looms, and keeping and maintaining them by journeymen and persons unskilful, to the decay of a great number of artificers which were brought up in the science of weaving, their families and households; some by engrossing [accumulation] of looms into their hands and possession, and letting them out at such unreasonable rents as the poor artificers are not able to maintain themselves; some also by giving much less wages and hire for the weaving and workmanship of cloth than in times past.' It therefore forbade clothiers who dwelt outside a city to keep more than one loom, or woollen weavers outside a city more than two looms. This measure did not affect urban centres and its operation was restricted to country districts, although in the eastern counties attempts were made to limit the number of looms even in towns. The efforts to check the development of a capitalist class proved unsuccessful; but the factory system failed to maintain itself in the face of strong social antipathy, the opposition of the government, and the absence of any vital economic necessity for the concentration of workmen under a factory roof. Occasionally, in the latter part of the eighteenth century, some substantial clothiers in the west country and in Yorkshire employed men in their own weaving sheds and so created a miniature factory. The advantages of the system were threefold. It enabled the employer to supervise in person the processes of manufacture; it prevented delay in the return of the work, which was wont to occur when a weaver wove in his own home for different masters; and it rendered more difficult any embezzlement of the raw material. Nevertheless the expense of building huge weaving sheds, coupled with the strenuous resistance of the weavers, checked the growth of a factory system until the introduction of machinery made it an economic necessity. The shearmen, however, generally worked in their employer's shop instead of their own homes, and thus they stood outside the domestic system of industry.

The clothiers often conducted business operations on a wide scale. Even in the fourteenth century there were big employers of labour, and in the Tudor epoch men like John Winchcombe and William Stumpe were prominent. In the seventeenth century a member of parliament told the House of Commons (1614) that he and his partner maintained above three thousand workmen; and in the eighteenth century Daniel Defoe relates that, as he was informed at Bradford in Wiltshire, 'it was no extraordinary thing to have clothiers in that country worth

from ten thousand to forty thousand pounds a man, and many
of the great families who now pass for gentry in those counties
have been originally raised from and built by this truly noble
manufacture.' The number of persons employed by a clothier
naturally varied considerably. Some clothiers utilized 150 or
even 200 weavers, but not all the weavers on an employer's
books worked for him alone. In addition to the weavers the
clothier kept in his service a large number of carders, spinners,
burlers, shearmen and others; thus a wealthy clothier might
employ altogether as many as 800 persons or more. It is
evident, then, that the capitalist employer was already the
outstanding figure in the textile industry long before the
'Industrial Revolution.'

For the disposal of his goods the clothier, unless he was a
merchant exporter, relied upon agents at Blackwell Hall who
were called factors. These factors fulfilled the same function in
the final stages of the cloth trade which the wool staplers served
in the early stages. They were middlemen who thrust themselves between the manufacturers and their customers (the
drapers or wholesale dealers). The factors were bitterly denounced as parasites on the industry. Intended originally to
assist the west country clothiers and Yorkshire merchants in
selling their cloth in London—for neither could afford the
time to journey to the metropolis and remain there until the
cloth was sold—they raised themselves to be 'the chief masters
of the clothing trade.' They became indispensable because they
not only disposed of the cloth in the London market, but advanced the clothier money on which interest was paid so long
as the goods lay on their hands unsold. The root of the mischief
was the long credit which the clothiers were forced to give to
the drapers, the standard rule being six months and even nine,
twelve and fifteen; this made them dependent on the factors
for advances. As a result of handling large funds and monopo-
lizing the sale of cloth the factors grew rich. They started almost
from nothing—'no more being required to set up a factor than
an ink-box and two quires of paper'—and accumulated fortunes
of 'five and ten thousand pounds and some of them forty and
fifty thousand pounds a man.' While the clothiers, it was said,

'lived poorly and got little or nothing the merchants lived splendidly and laid up money.' Accordingly it is not surprising to find the economic literature of the seventeenth and eighteenth centuries filled with denunciations of the factors. A pamphlet written in the form of a play[1] purported to show the contemptuous manner in which the factors, once the agents and servants of the clothiers, now treated their former masters. In one of the scenes the factors and clothiers dine together in a tavern. The factors sit apart at the head of the room, and after the dinner they propose that everyone should pay an equal share of the reckoning. The clothiers willingly agree but make the discovery that the factors had reserved for their own table the most expensive wines and viands; and the scene ends in great disorder.

The principal groups among the manual workers were weavers, spinners, wool-combers, and cloth-finishers.

The weavers in the west country were not independent producers; they worked for hire on material supplied by the capitalist. They contracted with the clothier to weave the yarn which he delivered to them into cloth of a certain size; they carried it to their homes and did the work under their own roofs; when the cloth was woven they took it back to their employer and received the price of their work. This is essentially the wage system since they had no property in the goods they manufactured. Yet though they did not own the material they usually owned their looms. The price of a loom varied—some cost two, three or four guineas, others even more; or a weaver might construct a loom with his own hands. The Weavers' Act of 1555 limited those who lived outside the old urban seats of industry to two looms, but the restriction was not generally observed. Some weavers kept as many as five or six looms under their roofs, chiefly when they had large families. As a rule they did not confine themselves to one master; they took work from several at once. The system had its advantages from the point of view of the operatives; if trade were dull with one clothier they might find work with another; they could pick and choose what kind of work they pleased; and it

---

[1] *The Beaux Merchant, A Comedy. By a Clothier* (? J. Blanch), 1714.

heightened their feeling of independence to have more than one string to their bow. To the employer the practice was inconvenient; the return of the work was sometimes delayed for weeks; and whenever trade was brisk he had no staff of workmen upon whose services he could rely exclusively.

Weaving was not confined to men. As we saw above, women played an important part in weaving just as they did in other branches. It was their recognized province:

> By day the web and loom
> And homely household talk shall be her doom.[1]

The employment of women was attacked in the fifteenth and sixteenth centuries; and indeed at one manufacturing centre (Cullompton in Devonshire) they were not allowed to learn weaving down to 1825; but as a rule their labour was not suppressed and some women earned by weaving as much as men. At Trowbridge and Bradford in Wiltshire in the eighteenth century two weavers out of every five were women. In the north of England also women and girls followed the occupation; it was usual, in any case, for the wife of a weaver to assist her husband in working the broad loom.

The weavers' earnings varied at different epochs and in different parts of the country. In the year of the Armada (1588) a Yorkshire weaver received barely fivepence a day, and a century later his wages had scarcely increased in spite of the great rise in prices due to the influx of American silver. In the eighteenth century weavers in general made seven to ten shillings a week. The real value of this sum, that is the purchasing power of money, may be measured by the following prices at Leeds in 1770—ten to eleven ounces of oatbread (the favourite food) could be bought for 1d.; eighteen to nineteen ounces of butter for 8d.; cheese was 4d. per pound; mutton, beef and pork 4d. per pound; veal 2½d. per pound; milk ½d. per pint in summer and 1d. or 1½d. in winter; house rent was 40s. a year and firing 20s.

Average earnings were affected by the amount of unemployment. Weavers were not employed all the year round; there

[1] Dryden.

were always periods when many were out of work. In a trade depression some employers might continue to give out yarn to weavers and prepare their cloth in anticipation of a revival of trade, but others waited for orders. In the west country it was not unknown for a weaver to be unemployed seventeen weeks together, and an unemployed artisan usually fared ill. In harvest time he might earn two meals and a shilling a day in the fields. Still the harvest comes but once a year; and as the textile workers in the west of England owned very little land they were often employed, when out of work, in labour on the roads or forced to break stones and wheel heavy loads. Even where rural employment was available the weaver would not find it a satisfactory substitute for weaving. Rural occupations were poorly remunerated and the weaver, living a sedentary life, was not adapted physically for an outdoor existence; moreover hard toil roughened his hands making him less fit for weaving—a fact overlooked by those who lay stress upon the opportunities for rural employment enjoyed by textile artisans prior to the 'Industrial Revolution.'

The law of apprenticeship had become obsolete by the eighteenth century, and few attempts were made to enforce it in courts of law. The majority of clothiers probably never heard of the Elizabethan Statute of Apprentices, and did not know that they could be punished for employing a workman who had not served a legal apprenticeship. Yet although the eighteenth-century weaver did not trouble himself about the technicalities of the law of apprenticeship, there was a well-understood difference between a 'legal' and an 'illegal' workman. A legal workman was a man who served round about seven years at a trade before he set up for himself. He need not be regularly 'indentured,' provided he was taught by someone who knew his business. Not only the legal but also the social character of apprenticeship underwent a change. Instead of the apprentice residing with his master as in the olden days it became an increasing practice, except in the case of parish apprentices, to pay the boy wages in lieu of board and lodging. A contract (1714), in which an apprentice bound himself to a Gloucester-shire weaver for four and a quarter years, stipulated that 'he should find himself in food, drink, lodging and apparel and might go home every Saturday to Monday; his wages were to be out of every shilling made by his master 2½d. in the first year, 3d. the second and third years, 4d. the fourth year.' This form of apprenticeship was sometimes known as 'colting' and closely resembled the journeyman system.

When the term of training was completed the apprentice became a journeyman. The number of journeymen employed by a master weaver depended upon his number of looms. Before Kay invented the fly shuttle two persons were required to work the broad loom, the master weaver and a journeyman, but often the weaver's wife or daughter or an apprentice supplied the place of a journeyman. In former times the journeyman was engaged for fixed periods, and the Statute of Apprentices (1563) made compulsory an engagement for twelve months; yet in the eighteenth century the journeyman might be engaged only to make a single piece of cloth. The method of payment was one-third of the price received by the master weaver from the clothier. In addition to his piece-rate earnings the journeyman received 'small beer, lodging and firing' where he had no home of his own. It was called his 'privilege' and was valued at a shilling a week. Altogether in the west country a journeyman in constant employment earned, exclusive of his 'privilege,' about a shilling a day and he worked fourteen or fifteen hours daily. After he had acquired by his industry a loom of his own, he was then able to set up as a master weaver.

The spinning of yarn was generally the work of women and children. It was peculiarly a female occupation, as is shown by the word 'spinster' now applied to an unmarried woman. The Book of Proverbs praises the virtuous woman as one who 'seeketh wool and flax and worketh willingly with her hands: she layeth her hands to the spindle and her hands hold the distaff.' An old English rhyme represents the division of labour among our primeval parents in the well-known couplet:

When Adam delv'd and Eve span
Who was then a gentleman?[1]

[1] Cf. Goneril in *King Lear:* 'I must change arms at home and give the distaff into my husband's hands.'

Pliny relates that at the nuptials of a Roman maiden a distaff dressed with wool and a spindle trimmed with thread were carried in the procession, presumably to put her in mind of a housewife's duties; and Langland's exhortation in *Piers the Plowman* shows that spinning was regarded in the middle ages as the natural employment of women:

> Wives and widows: wool and flax spinneth,
> Maketh cloth I counsel you, and kenneth so
>   your daughters.

Children were taught to spin from their earliest years. In mediaeval houses an apartment was sometimes reserved as a family spinning room. Often the work was carried on in the open air. On sunny days women and children would betake themselves with their spinning wheels to some chosen spot and there pursue their labours; even as late as the nineteenth century girls were to be found in the Highlands of Scotland herding on the hillside busily spinning with their distaffs. Spinning occupied all the leisure moments of those engaged in it; the hours were extremely long though the work was light. A tradition of north Germany contains a warning against spinning on Saturday evening. It tells of a woman who appeared after her death to a fellow-culprit, displaying her burning hand with the words:

> See what I in Hell have won
> Because on Saturday I spun.

In this country one day in the Calendar of Saints was named St. Distaff's Day. It was the morrow after Twelfth Day—that is, January 7—and it closed the season of Christmas festivities:

> Partly work and partly play
> You must on St. Distaff's Day.
> From the plough soon free your team,
> Then come home and fother them.
> If the maids a-spinning go,
> Burn the flax and fire the tow.
> Bring in pails of water then,
> Let the maids bewash the men.

Give St. Distaff all the right,
Then bid Christmas sport good-night.
And next morning everyone
To his own vocation.[1]

Sometimes the spinners worked on their own; they bought the raw material, spun it into yarn, and then carried it to the market for sale. As a rule they worked for hire on their employers' material—their employers being either clothiers, master wool-combers, or market spinners (that is, yarn makers). The spinners were scattered over the whole countryside, and 'spinning houses' or 'pack-houses' were established in the villages for the distribution of the wool. The village shop frequently served as the 'pack-house,' and the wool was conveyed to it by carriers or 'packmen;' hither the spinners repaired for their material and returned it after it was spun into yarn. Spinning was thus essentially a cottage industry, and clothiers were able to draw for their supply of labour upon a very extensive area. The worsted industry of the Norfolk towns, for instance, was fed with yarn not only by the eastern counties —Suffolk, Cambridge, Bedford and Hertford—but also by Yorkshire and Westmorland.

Hand-spinning had two serious drawbacks. The spinner often lacked the requisite technical skill; the yarn was therefore neither uniform in quality nor firm enough to stand the strain of the loom; and the cloth, as a result, was uneven in texture. It was not unknown for ten hands to be engaged on a single chain (warp), and since it was spun irregularly the thread was constantly breaking; a considerable portion of the weaver's time, in fact, was spent in repairing broken threads. The difficulty of exercising proper supervision over the spinners was heightened by the system under which the yarn was collected. They brought the yarn to the 'pack-house' in small quantities and were paid by instalment; fraudulent or indifferent spinners were thereby enabled to deliver inferior work without detection by the clothiers to whom the yarn was sent at intervals in large quantities. To remedy the spinners'

[1] Herrick.

deficiencies in technical skill it was proposed to set up spinning schools, where children could be taught the art of spinning by experienced teachers. In England spinning schools were established in some localities as part of the organization of poor relief, and here poor children were taught by 'spinning dames.' The second drawback of hand-spinning was the inadequacy of the supply. In spite of the multitude of spinners they were unable to furnish weavers with the requisite amount of yarn. 'There are not hands enough in England,' it was said in 1718, 'to spin all the wool that must be used in our manufactures.' It is estimated that one loom gave work to half a dozen spinners or more, and the progress of the textile industry was checked by a yarn famine. In farming districts the spinning was largely done in the winter, and here the weavers were gravely handicapped during the summer months. Much of their time was consumed in waiting for work. The difficulties arising from the shortage of yarn were aggravated after Kay's invention of the fly shuttle in 1733 increased the productive power of the weaver. Moreover the intermittent nature of the supply forced the makers, in the words of a contemporary writer, 'to calculate for a larger profit.' The adoption of machinery in spinning towards the end of the eighteenth century was stimulated by vivid experience of the shortcomings of the old hand-yarn manufacture.

The spinners were poorly paid for their toil. In the seventeenth and eighteenth centuries England's greatest industry rested on the basis of sweated labour. According to Arthur Young women at Leeds earned 2s. 6d. or 3s. a week; girls thirteen or fourteen years old 1s. 8d.; boys of eight or nine 2½d. a day; a boy of six 1d. a day. In most cases, no doubt, the earnings of a spinner were intended to serve as an addition to the family budget and not as her only source of income. 'The pay is not much,' said a Lancashire woman, 'but it helps to boil the pot.' A woman, as Fitzherbert wrote in the sixteenth century, 'cannot get her living honestly with spinning on the distaff but it stoppeth a gap.' None the less many had to depend upon their scanty earnings for their daily subsistence; and even the meagre pittance gained by a spinner, after working twelve hours a day, was liable to be reduced under various pretexts such as 'the dulness of trade' or 'the custom of the trade.' Another device of capitalist exploitation was to use false weights in weighing out the material to spinners. This was a legacy of mediaeval times which is alluded to in *Piers the Plowman*:

> My wife was a weaver, woollen cloth she made;
> She spake to her spinsters to spin it soft;
> But the pound weight that she paid by weighed
>   a quarter more
> Than my own balance did when I weighed fair.

The fact that the spinners were unorganized made them powerless to resist industrial oppression.

Two other classes of artisans engaged in the woollen industry merit attention: the wool-combers and the cloth-finishers. The wool-combers were in a better position than the weavers. Their numbers were limited and their work was more highly remunerated. They were not tied to a particular locality and were accustomed to travel about the country from place to place in search of employment. One reason for their roving life was that a large number were single men; and when work was scarce in their native town, they were not compelled to accept low wages to save themselves from starvation. During their wanderings they were kept by the institution to which they belonged; for the combers' union preferred to support its members in idleness rather than submit to a reduction of wages. When a wool-comber set out on his journeys he received from his club a certificate which testified that he was a member of the union, had behaved himself well and was an honest man. The certificate entitled him to relief from every wool-combers' society affiliated to his branch, and enabled him to 'travel the kingdom round, be caressed at each club, and not spend a farthing of his own or strike one stroke of work.'[1] Anyone convicted of fraud forfeited his claim to the certificate and the privileges which it conferred.

The cloth-finishers were also known as cloth-workers, cloth-dressers, shearmen, and croppers. The distinctive feature of this

---

[1] Cf. *The Song of the Rambling Wool-Combers*, who lived 'regardless of your pity.'

class was that their work was not performed at home as in the case of carders, spinners and weavers, but was done in a workshop. Hence their industry—in the eighteenth century—was not a cottage industry; they worked together in large bodies, three men and one boy being engaged on a piece of cloth. The cloth-finishers were employed in different ways. Sometimes a number of clothiers had their cloths dressed at the same shop, where a master dresser (as he was called) worked for them on commission and kept as many as forty or fifty men and boys. At other times the clothiers employed cloth-finishers under their own roofs. The story of Jack of Newbury represents the establishment of the great clothier as housing shearmen, rowers, fullers and dyers; and in Yorkshire the merchants, who bought the cloth in an unfinished state from the clothiers, often assumed direct responsibility for the final processes of the manufacture. The attempt of the clothiers and merchants to seize into their hands all the branches of the cloth manufacture was strenuously resisted by the master dressers and dyers.

The old domestic system of industry is often painted in very vivid colours. It is attractive, no doubt, to contemplate the artisan working in his own home, in the midst of his family, a free agent, not subject to the discipline of the factory bell, but at liberty to work or to play as the inclination seized him. In reality the domestic system, as it existed in the west, had grave defects.

To begin with, the hours of labour were very long. In the middle of the eighteenth century fourteen hours, including meals, constituted a normal working day; while some weavers worked as much as fifteen or sixteen hours a day. A Wiltshire weaver told a parliamentary committee, which was investigating the conditions of the woollen industry in 1803, that 'in winter we work as much by the candle as by daylight. I have worked from five to seven at night in winter and from four to nine in summer'—that is, fourteen hours a day in winter, seventeen in summer. Moreover the weavers often lived a long way from the clothier's house: some had several miles to walk in fetching and returning the work. This wasted a great deal of the weaver's time, especially since he served more than one employer.

In the eyes of the employers the worst defect of the domestic system was the embezzlement of the raw material. At all periods complaints were general that carders and spinners and weavers appropriated the wool given out to them. Detection was difficult and the numerous laws against embezzlement failed to check the practice. In Scotland spinners or weavers who defrauded their employers were ordered 'to be kept in prison till the market day, and there to stand in time of the market two hours with a paper mentioning their fault in great letters.' A popular Scottish rhyme depicts the evil end of weavers who had been hanged for stealing yarn:

> As I gaed up the Canongate
> And through the Nether-bow,
> Four and twenty weavers
> Were singing in a tow.
>
> The tow gae a crack,
> The weavers gae a girn.
> Fie, let me down again,
> I'll never steal a pirn.
>
> I'll ne'er steal a pirn,
> I'll ne'er steal a pow.
> Oh fie, let me down again,
> I'll steal nae mair frae you.[1]

One reason for the prevalence of embezzlement is to be found in the low wages paid by the clothier. Those who with difficulty kept body and soul together by working excessively long hours, spinning wool or weaving cloth, were tempted to eke out their miserable pittance by methods to which they may often have been driven by sheer pressure of want.

A universal trait of the domestic system throughout the country was the employment of children. In former times child labour was considered a good thing. Daniel Defoe records with

---

[1] *Gaed* = went. *Tow* = halter. *Gae* = gave. *Girn* = cry of pain. *Pirn* = a quill on which yarn was wound. *Pow* = (?) crab. *Nae mair* = no more.

G

pride that in his day (1724) there was not a child in Taunton or the neighbourhood above five years old 'but, if it was not neglected by its parents and untaught, could earn its own bread.' Under the domestic system children were put to work as soon as they were able to render any kind of service, and it was remarked upon when children of six were 'idle.' The younger folk assisted their elders in various ways. They fetched the bobbins, they wound or 'quilled' the spun yarn, they helped the weaver to prepare the loom for weaving, they learnt the preparatory processes like willeying, carding, scribbling and slubbing; and as they grew older they were able to spin and to weave—it was alleged to be very common for boys and girls to acquire the art of weaving by the time they were twelve years old. In some cases a child might go to school and work in the morning and evening. The daily earnings of children were usually small. Those who were four to eight years of age earned a penny at quilling, from eight to twelve they earned twopence to fourpence at spinning, and from thirteen to four-teen eightpence at weaving; but the rates of wages varied considerably in different parts of the country. As a rule children worked under the eyes of their parents, and in so far as the latter avoided exhausting toil the evils of child labour would be mitigated. Yet in earlier centuries children were not always treated humanely by their parents. One who was brought up under the domestic system declared that the days of his child-hood were 'really the days of infant slavery.' 'The creatures,' he said, 'were set to work as soon as they could crawl and their parents were the hardest of taskmasters.' On the whole it would appear that children were employed at an earlier age and for less wages than the majority of children employed in factories. In any case the use of child labour was not due to the introduction of machinery, and it was only the creation of the factory system which made it possible in the nineteenth century to abolish it.

When we pass from the west to the north of England we are confronted with a widely different kind of industrial society. The domestic manufacturers of Yorkshire, as the clothiers there were called, resembled neither the clothiers nor the master weavers of the west country—they differed from the latter because they owned not only their looms but also the material upon which they worked; they differed from the former because they were primarily manual craftsmen rather than entrepreneurs. None the less they were not wage-earners. They bought the wool from the dealers and in their own houses, assisted by their wives, children and journeymen, they worked it up through all the different stages and finally sold the manufactured cloth in the open market. The number of looms owned by a domestic manufacturer varied according to circumstances; at the end of the eighteenth century most clothiers had two and some three or more. The Yorkshire clothier, unlike the west country clothier, was himself a workman and wove in the loom. He was usually helped by his family, sometimes also by apprentices and journeymen. On an average he probably employed at least ten persons.

The family life of the West Riding clothier is portrayed in a colloquial poem 'descriptive of the Manners of the Clothiers' written about 1730. At the evening meal the master of the house gives instructions to his wife, apprentices and journeymen regarding the work of the morrow:

> Lads, work hard I pray,
> Cloth mun be pearked[1] next market day,
> And Tom mun go to-morn to t'spinners,
> And Will mun seek about for t'swingers,
> And Jack to-morn by time be rising
> And go to t'sizing mill for sizing.[2]
> And get your web and warping done
> That ye may get it into t'loom.
> Jo go give my horse some corn,
> For I design for t'Wolds to-morn.[3]
> So mind and clean my boots and shoon,
> For I'll be up i' t'morn right soon.
> Mary—there's wool—tak thee and dye it.

[1] *Pearked*=perched (*i.e.* tested for faults).
[2] *Sizing*=saturating the warp with paste.
[3] The purpose of his journey is to buy wool.

His wife objects that she has her house-work to do: 'To bake and swing and blend and milk, and bairns to school to send,' as well as 'washing up morn, noon, and neet.' But the husband retorts:

> All things mun aside be laid,
> When we want help about our trade.

The young folk are then left to themselves and they sit round the fire telling tales and 'merry jokes.'

> Till ten gives warning by the clock,
> Then up they start—to bed they run.

At five o'clock the next morning they commence again the day's round.

The institution of apprenticeship survived longer, in its traditional form, in the north of England than in the west. The Yorkshire clothier needed a thorough training in the various branches of the woollen industry—for though a man was generally employed on one operation, whenever it was necessary he could turn his hand to others as occasion might require. It was unusual for an apprentice to set up as a master immediately he was 'out of his time;' as a rule he became a journeyman. Sometimes the journeyman was hired by the year, in which case he worked the customary hours and received as wages eight to ten pounds annually in addition to his board; but payment by piece-work was more common. A striking feature of industrial conditions in Yorkshire was the good feeling existing between domestic manufacturers and their workmen. In a trade depression the former rarely dismissed their hands. 'Our men and masters,' a witness told a parliamentary committee, 'are in general so joined together in sentiment and, if I may be admitted to use the term, love to each other that they do not wish to be separated if they can help it. We always consider the masters and journeymen as one and our interests are reciprocal.' The Yorkshire clothier prided himself upon the fact that it was 'almost a thing unknown to discharge a workman for want of employment. Winter or summer, bad trade or good, we go on straight forwards' whether the stock was sold or left on their hands. 'I have been with domestic manufacturers when they were short of work,' said a journeyman, 'and they used to see about a job for me and if one couldn't be got I was continued.' On the other hand, when a clothier had extra orders, 'we ask another master perhaps whether he will spare us such a man to weave for us.'

The outstanding merit of the Yorkshire domestic system, apart from the friendly relations between masters and men, was the opportunity afforded to every workman of rising in the world. In the north of England it was not difficult for any wage-earner in the woollen industry to become a master. Every journeyman who was careful and persevering worked with the idea of saving up money 'by good economy,' and then setting up on his own as soon as he could. 'When I only got ten shillings a week,' said a successful clothier who began with one loom and ended with twenty-one, 'I saved one out of it.' The working clothier needed little capital; his utensils were either home-made or cheaply bought; and the raw material was readily obtained on credit.

Another element in the industrial society of the north was a class of merchants to whom the domestic manufacturers sold their cloth in an unfinished state. In the middle ages cloth was always exposed for sale in a public place on fixed days of the week, and it was an offence against the law to buy or sell cloth privately. When commodities were disposed of secretly the owner of the market went without his tolls, and the public sale of cloth also facilitated the work of inspectors (aulnagers) whose duty it was to see that the makers had observed the statutory regulations as to size and quality. In London the famous centre of the cloth trade was Blackwell Hall, and in other towns a site was reserved for the sale of cloth; for example, in the north the Thursday market of York, in the east the Worsted Seld of Norwich, in the west the Touker Street market of Bristol, among many others. In general, apart from Blackwell Hall, the system of public cloth markets retained its importance only in Yorkshire. The chief was Leeds where it was held originally upon the bridge of the river and later in the High Street. Vivid accounts of this market have come down

to us and they all dwell upon the same features: the long rows
of stalls covered with cloth, the manufacturers ranged behind
their stands, the merchants passing along and making purchases
in 'profound silence,' the bell ringing at the end of an hour to
indicate the close of the market. In the eighteenth century
several cloth halls were erected in Yorkshire towns to take the
place of the open market—at Halifax in 1700, at Wakefield in
1710, at Leeds in 1711. As industry developed more halls
might be necessary; a second white cloth hall was opened at
Leeds in 1755 and a third in 1775, while a hall for coloured
cloth was built in 1756. None but those who had been apprenticed or 'legally brought up' were allowed to purchase stands in
the official halls; and those who were not lawful clothiers used to
assemble in Potter's Field, whence originated yet another hall
bearing the significant title of Tom Paine hall.

The cloth exposed for sale in the Yorkshire markets was
bought in the rough state, fulled but undressed. The merchant
himself assumed responsibility for the final processes of cloth-
making; and the cloth was dressed in his own workshop or
committed to a master dresser. Here it underwent the various
processes known as cloth-working—raising and cropping the
nap until a smooth finish had been imparted to the surface.
The Yorkshire merchant was thus in a limited sense a manufacturer, an industrialist as well as a trading capitalist: ultimately he was destined to usurp the place of the domestic
clothier completely, and become master of the whole series of
operations from carding and spinning to fulling and dressing.

The oversea trade in cloth was in the hands of merchant
exporters, who were required to belong to a chartered company
that enjoyed a complete monopoly of traffic in the territorial
sphere assigned to it. The ideal of mediaeval commerce, which
lasted beyond the middle ages, was 'a well-ordered and ruled
trade' in which production was limited, prices were high and
stable, and commodities were well wrought. The Merchant
Adventurers, who shipped cloth to northern Europe, prided
themselves on the fact that they did 'keep up the price of our
commodities abroad by avoiding an over-glut, whereas when

trade is free many sellers will make wares cheap and of less estimation.' The system of chartered companies had certain advantages—it prevented excessive competition among merchants, which flooded the market with goods and lowered prices to the benefit of oversea buyers; it also enabled the government to control trade and advance the interests of the state as they were then understood. Its great drawback was that it retarded the expansion of foreign commerce, it curtailed competition and checked enterprise. Thus the Merchant Adventurers did not permit a member to export more than four hundred cloths during the first three years of membership; subsequently the number rose annually by fifty, so that in his fifteenth year he was able to export a thousand cloths. The enemies of the companies were the 'interlopers,' who were outside their fellowship yet 'intermeddled' with their business. They appealed to the traditional liberty of Englishmen and defied the companies' monopoly. The centre of the 'interlopers' was the west of England, where the clothiers resented the claim of London to handle the shipment of their cloth. The best method of pushing oversea trade developed into a thorny subject of controversy: but after the Revolution of 1688 the 'interlopers' triumphed. An act for encouraging the woollen manufacture allowed all persons to send cloth abroad freely, a saving clause reserving the monopoly of four companies only—the Levant, Eastland, Russia, and African.

Merchant exporters had commercial agents in all parts of the world; and we get interesting glimpses of the duties these factors (as they were called) were expected to perform in a series of instructions drawn up about the year 1582 for the guidance of an English factor in Turkey. The writer assumes as an axiom that 'of the many things that tend to the common benefit of the state no one thing is greater than clothing.' He proceeds: 'This realm yieldeth the most fine wool, the most soft, the most durable in cloth, [and] there is no commodity of this realm that may set so many poor subjects on work as this doth, that doth bring in so much treasure and so much enrich the merchant and so much employ the navy of this realm, as this commodity of our wool doth. Ample and full vent [sale] of this noble and rich commodity is it that the commonwealth of this realm doth require.' After this exordium the factor is told how he may best serve his country. 'Forasmuch as it is reported that the woollen cloths dyed in Turkey be most excellently•dyed, you shall send home unto this realm certain pieces of shred to be brought to the Dyers' Hall there to be showed; partly to remove out of their heads the too great opinion they have conceived of their own cunning, and partly to move them for shame to endeavour to learn more knowledge. To amend the dyeing of England learn to know all the materials and substances that the Turks use in dyeing, be they herbs, plants, berries or mineral matter. If you shall find that they make any cloth of any kind not made in this realm, that is there of great use, then bring of the same into this realm some mowsters [samples] that our people may fall into the trade and prepare the same for Turkey. For the more kinds of cloth we can devise to make, the more ample vent of our commodity we shall have, and the more sale of the labour of our poor subjects that else for lack of labour become idle and burdensome to the commonweal. And in England we are in our clothing trade to frame ourselves according to the desires of foreign nations, be it that they desire thick or thin, broad or narrow, long or short, white or black. Thus,' concludes the writer, 'may you help to drive idleness, the mother of most mischief, out of the realm and win you perpetual fame and the prayer of the poor, which is more worth than all the gold of Peru and of all the West Indies.'

CHAPTER SIX

State Control

THE WOOLLEN AND WORSTED industries from their infancy were the subject of state regulation. As the staple product of the realm their prosperity was always considered a matter of the greatest national importance. The clothiers succeeded, in the words of Adam Smith, 'in convincing the wisdom of the nation that the safety of the commonwealth depends upon the prosperity of their particular manufacture.' The latter was 'petted and favoured' (in Huskisson's phrase) by the legislature which lavished upon it the most unremitting care and attention, and created for its protection an elaborate code of industrial and commercial legislation. We shall describe first the commercial regulations, and it will be seen how every interest in the country was rendered subservient to the assumed needs of the cloth trade; how agriculture and commerce were shackled, Ireland and the colonies hampered in their development, in order that the woollen manufacturer might have an adequate supply of raw material and the undisputed possession of markets at home and abroad.

Of the various links in the chain of protection designed for the safeguarding of wool textiles the most important was the prohibition of the export of wool. This, as we have shown above,[1] was a permanent feature of England's economic policy for two hundred years: it lasted from the early seventeenth to the early nineteenth century. The embargo on wool was combined in the eighteenth century with an embargo on the emigration of skilled artisans. In earlier ages England reaped great benefit from the settlement of aliens, and she was now anxious to prevent other nations using her technical skill to build up their own industries. In the troubled reign of Charles I textile workers in Norfolk and Suffolk sought refuge in Holland from religious persecution, and more emigrated during the

[1] Part I.

Civil War probably owing to want of employment. While some went under compulsion, others were enticed abroad: Holland, Germany, France, Portugal and Spain in particular encouraged the settlement of English artificers. An act of 1719 endeavoured to check the movement by imposing heavy penalties on those who induced workmen to leave the country and teach the arts of cloth-making in foreign lands. 'Divers ill-disposed persons, as well foreigners as subjects of this kingdom by confederacy with foreigners, have of late drawn away and transported several artificers and manufacturers of and in wool out of his majesty's dominions into foreign countries, by entering into contracts with them to give greater wages and advantages than they have or can reasonably expect within this kingdom, and by making them large promises.' The penalties did not serve as a deterrent and the outcry persisted that 'foreigners decoy our manufacturers.' The restraints on emigration, which lasted down to 1825, were supplemented by an embargo on the export of tools which was not finally removed until 1843.

To confine English raw material and English textile workers to England was only one part of the system of protection: the other part was to confine the English people to English manufactures by enforcing the consumption of domestic products. The use of native cloth was therefore enjoined on all as a patriotic duty. As far back as the thirteenth century the nation was urged not to 'seek over-precious garments' but to rest content with home-spun garments. A strong agitation in favour of the compulsory wearing of cloth made within the realm sprang up in the seventeenth century. Just as Queen Elizabeth established a compulsory Lent on certain days in the week in order to foster the fishing trade, so her successor endeavoured to compel his subjects to wear native instead of foreign textiles. A bill 'for the better vending of the cloth of this kingdom' was introduced into Parliament in 1621 but met with some opposition. 'It is hard,' said a member, 'to make a law whereby we shall not know our wives from our chambermaids.' Others however approved the measure, and suggested the addition of a clause 'that none under the degree of a baron should mourn in anything but cloth.' After the Restoration the agitation was renewed. The 'Flannel Act' in 1667 enacted that the dead must be buried in woollen cloth—'forcing the dead,' as Arthur Young said, 'to consume what the living were inadequate to purchase.'

> Since the living would not bear it,
> They should, when dead, be forc'd to wear it.

The following year (1668) the House of Commons presented an address to the king praying him to encourage the wearing of domestic manufactures 'by his own example and his queen's.' Recognizing that practice is better than precept, it was also resolved 'that the House begin themselves to show a good example herein to the nation.' A subsequent resolution (1678) enjoined 'all persons whatsoever to wear no garment, stockings or other sort of apparel but what is made of sheep's wool only from the Feast of All Saints to the Feast of the Annunciation of Our Lady inclusive.' These efforts to promote the compulsory use of native cloth were renewed after the Revolution. In 1698 the House of Commons ordered the insertion of a clause 'that all magistrates, judges, students of the universities and all professors of the common and civil law do wear gowns made of the woollen manufacture.' In short, as a pamphleteer wrote at the beginning of the eighteenth century, 'both the Living and the Dead must be wrapt in woollen, indeed no other law is wanted but only one—that our perukes should be made of wool.'

The woollen manufacturers, who claimed by 'prescription and possession' a monopoly of their industry, regarded the domestic market as their natural preserve. They sought therefore to prevent the importation of goods made abroad which competed with commodities produced at home. Successful in their efforts to exclude foreign wool textiles, they proceeded to carry on a campaign against all foreign textiles which might serve as a substitute for English woollen fabrics. The popularity of Indian silks and muslins caused great alarm lest they should become 'the general wear' and 'eat up our manufactures.'

Our Ladies all were set a gadding,
After these Toys they ran a madding.
And like gay Peacocks proudly strut it
When in our Streets along they foot it.

'I question not,' said one writer, 'but we shall have cotton cloth
and knaves to make it a fashion and fools enough to wear it.'
The use of cotton, it was complained, put 'all degrees and orders
of woman-kind into disorder and confusion' since the lady
'cannot well be known from her chambermaid.' 'The general
fancy of the people,' wrote Defoe, 'runs upon East India goods
to that degree that the chints and painted calicoes which before
were only made use of for carpets, quilts, etc. and to clothe
children and ordinary people, became now the dress of our
ladies; and such is the power of a mode as we saw our persons
of quality dressed in Indian carpets which but a few years
before their chambermaids would have thought too ordinary
for them; the chints were advanced from lying upon their
floors to their backs; from the footcloth to the petticoat; and
even the queen herself at this time was pleased to appear in
China and Japan, I mean China silks and calico. Nor was this
all but it crept into our houses and bedchambers; curtains,
cushions, chairs and at the last beds themselves were nothing
but calicoes or Indian stuffs; and in short almost everything that
used to be made of wool or silk, relating either to the dress of
the women or the furniture of our houses, was supplied by the
Indian trade.' The English workman, it was said, could not
compete with Eastern labour because 'the people in India are
such slaves as to work for less than a penny a day whereas ours
here will not work under a shilling.'

The duel between the woollen manufacturers and the powerful East India Company ended in the triumph of the former.
Yielding to the agitation Parliament in 1700 forbade the use of
wrought silks made in India, Persia or China, as well as of
calicoes 'painted, dyed, printed or stained there.' The exclusion
of Indian silks and printed calicoes had an unexpected result, for
it encouraged the English cotton manufacturers to seize their
opportunity to capture the market from which their Indian

competitors had been expelled. 'As if this nation was never to want a set of men to undo her,' complained the indignant weavers, 'no sooner were the East India chints and printed calicoes prohibited from abroad but some of Britain's un- natural children, whom we call drapers, set all their arts to work to evade the law of prohibition, to employ people to mimic the more ingenious Indians and to legitimate the griev- ance by making it a manufacture.' Appeals were made to women to discard the new fashions. The weavers raised a great clamour and attacked in the open streets those who wore cotton dresses—the 'calico madams' or 'calico Picts' as they were called—even tearing the clothes off their backs. Parlia- ment was forced to pass another act (1721) condemning the use of printed painted calicoes, since 'the wearing and using [of calicoes] does manifestly tend to the great detriment of the woollen and silk manufactures of this kingdom.' In this way the infant cotton industry was sacrificed to the woollen industry in order that nothing might impair the prosperity of the leading manufacture of the realm.[1]

In their efforts to secure the undisputed control of the domestic market the clothiers found themselves involved in controversies not only over the East India trade but over Ireland and the colonies. The Irish farmers had been forbidden in 1667 to export cattle to England so that the English farmer should have no competitor in the home market; they therefore turned their attention to grazing. As a result wool and meat became plentiful and cheap, and this abundance of raw mat- erial coupled with cheapness of living attracted artisans from the west of England. Irish competition was dreaded owing to the low price of labour; and the clothiers, alarmed at the new development, made strong protests that Ireland was under- mining their trade. Both Houses of Parliament petitioned the king that 'the wealth and power of this kingdom do in a great measure depend on the preserving the woollen manufacture as much as is possible entire to this realm,' and 'it becomes us

[1] Subsequently the 'Manchester Act' (1736) expressly permitted the use of printed fustians made of linen and cotton, provided the warp was entirely linen yarn.

like our ancestors to be jealous of the establishment and the increase therof elsewhere.' The outcry bore fruit in the act of 1699 which prohibited the export of Irish wool textiles except to England. Thus 'the Irish woollen fabrics,' in the words of Arthur Young, 'were destroyed by one of the most infamous statutes that ever disgraced a legislature.' A generation after its enactment it was said to have 'laid the foundations of all the misfortunes of both kingdoms. It drove abroad all our [*i.e.* Irish] woollen manufacturers who set up in different countries,' and—so ran the current opinion—it 'taught our neighbours to steal from us a manufacture we entirely engrossed before.' A writer pointed out that the English persecution in trade, in causing an exodus of Ireland's most industrious sons, had the same effect as the French persecution in religion. He showed the fallacy of the argument on which the suppression of the Irish woollen industry had been based. Assuming that Ireland did work cheaper than Yorkshire or Lancashire, 'would it hurt the British Empire more than it hurts her that Yorkshire or Lancashire should work cheaper than Devonshire or Cornwall? Can any man of open understanding consider Ireland but in the light of four or five great counties added to England advantageously for water carriage cut by a large navigable river?' To compensate Ireland for the injury done to her woollen manufacture, she was promised 'countenance, favour and protection' for her linen manufacture that it might become 'the general trade of that country as effectually as the woollen manufacture is and must be of England.' The English plantations in America were treated in a similar way, for one clause of the act of 1699 ordered that 'no wool, woollen yarn, cloth, serge, bays, kersies, says, friezes, druggets, cloth-serges, shalloons, or any other drapery, stuff or woollen manufactures whatsoever' should be exported from the colonies or even transported from one colony to another. The purpose of the restriction was to safeguard the English woollen trade with the American colonies, which was considerable inasmuch as it accounted for one-half the value of the total exports of English manufactures to the plantations.

The policy of protection was designed to give the woollen manufacturers the sole monopoly of the home market. Its application to the foreign market raised a controversy which lasted for nearly three centuries. The root of the trouble lay in the cleavage of interests between the trading and industrial capitalists. The merchant exporters demanded the right to ship cloth abroad in a raw state, undyed and unfininished. Their claim brought them into sharp collision with the cloth-finishers who importuned the government incessantly. Yet though the export of white cloth was repeatedly forbidden by statute, the prohibition proved ineffective. Accordingly attempts were made to foster a native dyeing industry. The most famous was Alderman Cockayne's 'unhappy project,' whereby all cloth was to be dyed and dressed at home before being allowed to leave the kingdom. James I granted him (1614) a patent for dyeing coupled with an embargo on the tran-shipment of cloth in an unfinished state. When the Merchant Adventurers pronounced the scheme unworkable, their privi-leges were suspended. The effects of this ill-starred venture soon became manifest. The clothiers complained that their cloth lay on their hands unsold; the cloth-finishers protested that they were in a worse plight than before. The scheme was per-force abandoned (1617)—in spite of Bacon's counsel to 'blow a horn to let the Flemings know your majesty will not give over the chase'—and the king confessed that 'time discovereth many inabilities which cannot first be seen.' The question came again to the front after the Revolution when, in order to remove any doubts as to the exact legal position, the export of white cloth was expressly sanctioned by law in 1707. Although divided on the question of the export of white cloth, manufac-turers and merchants alike recognized the importance of pushing the woollen trade overseas, and in this their efforts were warmly seconded by the government. Henry VII, in particular, concluded numerous commercial treaties intended to provide an outlet for wool textiles. The most memorable was the Magnus Intercursus (1496), which ensured a free market for the sale of English cloth in the Netherlands. Indeed one reason why the Tudors encouraged voyages of discovery was to find new markets for our woollen fabrics. Another notable treaty was the famous Methuen Treaty made with Portugal in 1703, which permitted the entry of English goods on condition that the wines of Portugal were admitted into England at two-thirds of the duty levied on French wines. 'The preserving our looms and the rents of Great Britain,' contended *The British Merchant*, 'was of greater consequence to the nation than gratifying our palates with French wine.'

While the policy of the government was mainly concerned with advancing the interests of the producer, yet at least on one occasion it intervened on behalf of the consumer. A fifteenth-century statute (1489) fixed the retail prices of cloth: 'Forasmuch as drapers, tailors and other in the city of London and other places within this realm, that use to sell woollen cloth at retail by the yard, sell a yard of cloth at excessive price having unreasonable lucre to the great hurt and impoverishment of the king's liege people, buyers of the same, against equity and good conscience,' the maximum retail price of cloth grained was fixed at 16s. a broad yard and 'out of the grain' at 11s. a yard.

The protective policy of the state, inspired by the purpose of safeguarding native manufacturers from foreign competition, was maintained down to the nineteenth century when the principles of *laissez-faire* were applied to commerce as they had already been applied to industry in the eighteenth century. In 1824 the export of wool was legalized; the following year the duty on imported cloth was reduced from 50 to 15 per cent. and subsequently abolished. In thus withdrawing the protection which wool textiles had enjoyed for many centuries, the state abandoned the most tenacious doctrine of its former economic creed.[1] The manufacturers predicted that the export of wool would extinguish the export trade in cloth. The prophecy was signally falsified. Although under free trade they were no longer sheltered from external rivalry, their oversea trade was not destroyed. Owing to the perfection of the machinery and the skill of the manufacturers who were now forced to rely upon

[1] The growth of the English wool textile industry under free trade is reflected in the immense increase in wool consumption.

their own ingenuity, woollen exports expanded in spite of the competition of the cotton industry.

State control of the woollen and worsted industries was not confined to the commercial sphere: it was also manifested in two other spheres—the processes of manufacture and general labour conditions.

In the domain of production the minutest rules were framed prescribing the quality of the materials, the use of mechanical appliances and the form of the finished article. Nowadays a manufacturer is free to make cloth as he pleases—long or short, fine or coarse. In earlier times an intricate network of national regulations was devised in order to standardize the making of cloth, that is, to establish a uniform standard of quality and dimensions. In respect of quality it was forbidden to mingle different kinds of wool in the same cloth—for example, to use lamb's wool or flocks (the refuse of wool) with ordinary sorts of wool—or to employ other fraudulent methods of manufacture. The nature of these malpractices is disclosed in the complaint of a sixteenth-century Parliament that 'clothiers study rather to make many than to make good cloths [and] instead of sub- stantial making of cloth do practise sleight and slender making —some by mingling of yarns of diverse spinnings in one cloth; some by mingling fell wool and lamb's wool, or either of them, with fleece wool; some by putting too little stuff; some by taking them out of the mill before they be full thicked; some by overstretching them upon the tenter and then stopping with flocks such breaks as shall be made by means thereof; finally by using so many subtle sleights [tricks] and untruths as when the cloths so made be put in the water to try them, they rise out of the same neither in length nor breadth as they ought to do.' Despite a stream of repressive enactments the legislature failed to extirpate the abuses. They still flourished in the seven- teenth century, when John May (an aulnager's deputy) enumerated in detail the deceits practised in his day: the mixing of different 'sorts' of wool which make the cloth uneven, as well as the frauds perpetrated in weaving, fulling, dyeing and finishing—such as utilizing a coarser yarn for the middle than

H

the ends of the cloth, 'which is so far as is commonly the merchant or buyer looks into them.'

The system of statutory dimensions was dictated partly in
the interests of consumers and partly to prevent traders de-
frauding the customs by exporting cloth of excessive length.
Inaugurated as early as the twelfth century and embodied in
Magna Carta, it was in existence as late as the eighteenth
century. In practice the 'assize of cloth' was largely a dead
letter notwithstanding the appointment of state officials known
as aulnagers, whose functions were to test the measurements
and quality of every piece of cloth, affixing a seal when the
cloth was sound or confiscating it when defective, and thereby
ensuring uniformity of 'length, breadth, weight and goodness.'
Furthermore it was found difficult to stamp out the custom of
stretching cloth unduly, which was liable to produce unfortu-
nate effects. 'If a gentleman make a livery for his man, in the
first shower of rain it may fit his page for bigness!' An act of
parliament even sought to prohibit the use of tenter-frames on
which cloth, after being fulled, was stretched in the open air
to dry: but in the face of the opposition of the manufacturers
this unpopular measure proved short-lived.[1]

The policy of industrial supervision harmonized with the
age-old tradition that the national economy should be 'orderly
governed.' But in the later seventeenth century economists
were beginning to proclaim the doctrine of *laissez-faire* that
'industry has its first foundation in liberty.' The policy of
standardizing industry was severely condemned by an eminent
authority Sir Josiah Child: 'All our laws that oblige our people
to the making of strong substantial (and as we call it loyal)
cloth of a certain length, breadth and weight—if they were duly
put into execution—would in my opinion do more hurt than
good because the humours and fashions of the world change,
and at some times in some places (as now in most) slight, cheap
light cloth will sell more plentifully and better than that which
is heavier, stronger and truer wrought; and if we intend to have
the trade of the world we must imitate the Dutch, who make
the worst as well as the best of all manufactures, that we may

[1] 1598–1624.

be in a capacity of serving all markets and all humours.' He recommended that clothiers should be left at liberty 'to make what cloth and stuffs they please, how they will, where and when they will, of any length or sizes.'

The Revolution of 1688 was followed, in this as in other directions, by a complete relaxation of industrial restraints. 'As the worthy makers of those good laws are now asleep,' it was complained in 1691, 'so are their laws too and every man may make his cloth at his own choice.' The aulnage survived only as an instrument of extortion—'very burdensome to the subject and a great hindrance to the woollen trade'—and its officials did not trouble themselves about the size and quality of the cloth but were content merely to enforce payment of the fees. The manufacturers themselves affixed the seals on their cloths without submitting them for inspection. The original design of the institution was entirely lost sight of when the makers assumed 'an uncontrolled liberty to make bad cloth of what materials they will;' and in 1724 the aulnage expired. A few years later (1738) Parliament openly discarded the system of standard measurements in Yorkshire in the case of narrow woollen cloths and in 1765 in the case of broad woollen cloths. At the opening of the nineteenth century a clothier told a parliamentary committee that 'at this time we make goods to suit every customer and every clime.' The attempt to standardize wool textiles was thus necessarily abandoned. It was manifestly impossible to manufacture cloths according to statutory measurements in view of the variety of fabrics exported abroad to meet the tastes of foreign buyers; nor was it considered imperative to prevent the straining and stretching of cloth, because the manufacturer was the one most interested in maintaining the credit of his cloth and therefore the most concerned not to stretch or strain it injuriously; while, lastly, the use of various ingredients forbidden by law was now required owing to improvements in the art of dyeing. The argument in short was that, however essential statutory control might have been in earlier times to give credit to the industry by preventing abuses, competition could henceforth be trusted to secure this end. 'The interest of the seller,' ran the current maxim of trade, 'is sufficient security to the buyer for fair dealing.'[1]

The industrial code regulating the general conditions of labour embraced wages, technical training and unemployment.

The grievance of low wages was as old as the capitalist system itself. In the sixteenth century the Suffolk and Essex weavers attributed their destitute state to a conspiracy of the 'rich men [the clothiers] to hold and pay one price for weaving of cloths,' and a price which was not enough to support their families even by working day and night, holy days and work days. In 1621 a member of parliament complained in the House of Commons that clothiers 'give not the poor competent wages—threepence a day and no more to divers.' A famous ballad, which is said to have been chanted about the streets in the time of Charles II, recited in rude rhymes the grievances of the workers in cloth against their employers. It is entitled *The Clothier's Delight, Or the Rich Men's Joy and The Poor Men's Sorrow, Where is exprest the craftiness and subtility of many clothiers by beating down their workmen's wages.* The opening verses run as follows:

Of all sorts of callings that in England be,
There is none that liveth so gallant as we;
Our trading maintains us as brave as a Knight,
We live at our pleasure and take our delight;
We heapeth up riches and treasure great store,
Which we get by griping and grinding the poor.
And this is a way for to fill up our purse,
Although we do get it with many a curse.

[1] In the eighteenth century a curious legend was industriously circulated concerning an elaborate fraud perpetrated on the Russian government. In 1724 'an able merchant did declare to the House of Commons the abuses [in English cloth] he himself had experienced, and that he had been concerned in clothing the army of Russia with the Yorkshire cloth, but that the cloth was so ill-managed that by one shower of rain upon a day of review the clothing of the whole army shrunk to such a degree that it brought discredit upon the cloth and lost the trade absolute.' The story was repeated at intervals in the eighteenth and nineteenth centuries, connected with various historical personages, and lost nothing in the re-telling.

Throughout the whole kingdom, in country and town,
There is no danger of our trade going down;
So long as the Comber can work with his comb,
And also the Weaver work with his lomb;
The Tucker and Spinner that spins all the year,
We will make them to earn their wages full dear.
    And this is a way for to fill up our purse,
    Although we do get it with many a curse.

In former ages we us'd to give
So that our workfolks like farmers did live;
But the times are altered, we will make them know
All we can for to bring them all under our bow;
We will make [them] to work hard for sixpence a day,
Though a shilling they deserve if they had their just pay.
    And this is a way for to fill up our purse,
    Although we do get it with many a curse.

The famous Statute of Apprentices (1563) ordered the justices of the peace in every county and city at the annual easter sessions to 'rate and appoint' the wages of labourers and artificers. There was some room for doubt whether it applied to textile workers, and in 1597 the magistrates were empowered 'to rate wages of any labourers, weavers, spinsters and workmen or workwomen whatsoever.' The act of 1597 was confirmed in 1604 with two significant additions—a justice who was also a clothier was not allowed to be a 'rater of wages for any artisan that dependeth upon the making of cloth;' and penalties were imposed upon any employer who paid less than the authorized wages. The act of 1604 was thus the first minimum wage act on the English statute-book. The system of assessment of wages was evidently popular among the weavers and spinners who pressed for its enforcement. The justices doubtless lacked the necessary technical qualifications for framing complicated piece-lists; and these were often drafted by a joint committee of clothiers and weavers, and submitted to the justices for ratification. A noteworthy instance of state intervention, 'for the general good of the whole commonwealth,' was the issue of a proclamation in 1636 ordering that in view

of the increase in the 'reel-staff'—'a fifth or sixth part longer
than had been accustomed'—the wages of spinners were to be
increased 'after the rate of twopence in the shilling more than
heretofore they have had paid unto them,' and 'all labourers and
other artificers employed about the trade of clothing and yarn-
making should have the like increase of wages.'

Connected with low wages was a practice which persisted
for many centuries, namely, the payment of truck wages.
Combers, spinners and weavers were often obliged by their
employers to take most of their wages in provisions or goods
which were rated at extravagant prices. Some clothiers forced
their weavers to become their tenants and to pay high rents for
their houses whether they occupied them or not; and others
made them buy their bread and other necessities at particular
shops. Another device was to defer the payment of wages until
they amounted to a considerable sum, and then compel the workpeople to take promissory notes payable at a future date; this not
only drove the workmen into debt but they had to forfeit part of
their earnings in order to get the notes discounted. The workers
kept up a ceaseless stream of protests against these abuses, and for
centuries the legislature enacted laws against them.

The intervention of the state was also demanded on behalf
of unemployed artisans. Unemployment is not a modern
phenomenon: in the cloth manufacture it is as old as the sixteenth century. Shakespeare alludes to it in *King Henry VIII*:

> Upon these taxations
> The clothiers all, not able to maintain
> The many to them longing, have put off
> The spinsters, carders, fullers, weavers; who,
> Unfit for other life, compell'd by hunger
> And lack of other means, in desperate manner
> Daring the event to the teeth, are all in uproar
> And danger serves among them.

Unemployment was caused by seasonal fluctuations and deficiency of water-power as well as by wars and tariffs—for instance
in the seventeenth century France, Holland and Sweden
adopted a protectionist policy to encourage their own industries.

The intervention of the government under the Tudors and Early Stuarts took various forms. First, it sought to secure continuity of employment through long engagements. In the middle ages it was not unknown to engage textile workers for three or four years; and the Statute of Apprentices (1563) required a minimum of one year (sometimes even in the eighteenth century they were hired in Yorkshire for twelve months). Second, it insisted that clothiers should not turn their employees adrift in periods of depression and that merchants should take unsold cloth off the manufacturers' hands. It repeatedly laid down the principle that those who gained by their trade in prosperous times were not at liberty to discard it in times of stress. An early example of the pressure brought to bear by the government upon clothiers and merchants alike occurred in 1528 when the trade in Flanders was interrupted by the outbreak of war. The clothiers were urged to keep their workfolk in employment, but they declared that they could not hold out more than two or three weeks unless the merchants continued to buy as usual. Wolsey summoned the merchants before him and thus addressed them: 'Sirs, the king is informed that you use not yourselves like merchants but like graziers and artificers; for when the clothiers do daily bring cloths to your market for your ease to their great cost and there be ready to sell them, you of your wilfulness will not buy them as you have been accustomed to do. What manner of men be you? I tell you that the king straitly commandeth you to buy their cloths as beforetime you have been accustomed to do, upon pain of his high displeasure.'

One of the most memorable depressions in the annals of the English textile industries began in 1620 and lasted four to five years. Exports declined by one-third; the price of wool fell; clothiers, even those reputed the wealthiest, were brought to the verge of bankruptcy; and unemployment was widespread. In one Wiltshire town forty-four looms stood idle for half a year—'by which means eight hundred persons, twenty at the least for each loom[1] in weaving, spinning and spooling, are now

[1] Estimates of the number of persons to whom each loom gave employment are conflicting.

miserably distressed for want of employment.' The distress was general throughout the kingdom: 'The whole commonwealth suffereth,' said a royal edict. Many thousands of spinners, weavers, fullers and cloth-workers were affected and disturbances seemed likely. 'We much fear,' wrote the justices of Gloucestershire to the Privy Council, 'that the peace hereof will be very shortly endangered notwithstanding all the vigilance we use or can use to the contrary' since workmen 'do wander, beg and steal and are in case to starve as their faces (to our great griefs) do manifest.' The unemployed went in groups to the houses of the rich demanding food and money, and seized provisions in the market-place. The Privy Council actively bestirred itself. It issued a circular letter to the justices of the 'clothing' counties, enjoining them to call the clothiers together and require the latter to keep their workfolk in employment. In some cases the justices were able to report that the employers were fully alive to their responsibilities. 'The clothiers here do yet continue to keep their poor in work as in former times they have done, although it hath been to their great losses; and so they are contented to do as long as they may occupy their trade without undoing of themselves.' Money was borrowed to pay wages; and it was recorded that 'one Will Bennett, a very ancient and good clothier, doth offer to live by brown bread and water rather than his great number of poor people should want work if he had means to keep them in work.' Other measures were taken to deal with the situation. Merchants were ordered to buy up as much cloth as possible, and wool dealers to sell wool at moderate prices; clothiers were protected from the importunity of their creditors; the justices were instructed to raise a fund, where necessary, to put the unemployed on work. Finally in 1622 a commission, composed of twelve persons, was set up to ascertain the causes of and remedies for the decay of trade; and two representatives of the clothiers of each 'clothing' county were summoned to London to give evidence before it. This commission, the first of its kind to make a detailed investigation of the causes of unemployment, drew up a comprehensive report reflecting the diversity of opinions expressed by the different interests consulted. The chief causes were alleged to be 'the making of cloth in foreign parts,' the heavy duties levied on exported cloth, the monopoly of the Merchant Adventurers, the war in Germany, 'the too little use of wearing cloth at home and the too much of silks and foreign stuffs.' The incidents we have cited do not stand alone, and it was in fact a recognized practice for workpeople out of employment to solicit the intervention of judges of the high courts or the local magistrates.

The responsibility for the technical training of weavers and shearmen had rested in the middle ages with the gilds. The custom of seven years' apprenticeship was general. It was enforced by statute as early as 1495 in the case of the shearmen of Norwich and in 1552 for the weavers of broad woollen cloths; eventually in 1563 it was made compulsory on all artisans. There were also legal restrictions as to the number of apprentices whom a master might keep. Thus the act of 1497 forbade worsted weavers to employ more than two apprentices at a time, and the Statute of Apprentices (1563) compelled every master in the cloth-making industry who had three apprentices to take on a journeyman. These laws, while intended to protect the journeyman from the competition of cheap labour and to ensure that the cloth was not spoilt by the inferior workmanship of half-trained assistants, set limits to the growth of industrial capitalism; and the latter in addition was kept in check by restrictions on the number of looms permitted to each weaver.

The Civil War profoundly affected the economic life of the country. It destroyed the power of the absolute monarchy, and this reacted upon labour conditions. The industrial legislation of the sixteenth century was allowed to fall into disuse. The Revolution of 1688 completed the process of disintegration, and Parliament came directly under the influence of the capitalist class which now demanded its liberation from the shackles of state control. The system of wage assessment died out and in 1757 it was legally discarded in the premier industry of the country, whereby the principles of *laissez-faire* received legislative sanction half a century before they were adopted as the authoritative basis of state action. As regards unemployment the government, after the Revolution, no longer required the clothiers to keep their men employed in times of trade depression and distress was relieved through the machinery of the poor law. Furthermore industrial capitalism claimed the right not only to make its own contract with labour concerning wages and length of service without interference, but also to draw freely on an unlimited supply of labour whether trained or not. The survival of apprenticeship after the Revolution became a matter of local custom rather than state compulsion, for Parliament openly abandoned any pretence at enforcement.

The changed attitude of the state towards the wages problem and the technical training of workmen was one of the factors in the rise of trade unionism. Capital and labour were no longer controlled by an external authority, and were set free to determine the general conditions of employment according to their respective strength. The workers in wool found that they must depend upon their own efforts for the maintenance of 'the standard of life;' and the Revolution, which brought to a final close the era of benevolent autocracy, was soon followed by an outburst of trade union activity.

The combinations formed among textile artisans in the eighteenth century were the forerunners of the great trade unions of the nineteenth century. The ostensible purpose of these associations was to serve as benefit clubs for the relief of the sick. In Gloucestershire, for instance, the members of a club paid twopence a week and received six shillings a week in times of sickness. However benefit clubs easily develop into trade societies, for when men who are engaged in the same occupation meet together at regular intervals they inevitably begin to discuss trade grievances. Our knowledge of the early trade union movement is derived mainly from the accounts given by the employers, which are naturally biased. In one town (Tiverton), it was alleged, the wool-combers and weavers 'have combined and formed themselves into clubs and unlawful assemblies, and have taken on themselves an arbitrary power to ascertain their wages in their respective businesses and trades;

by means whereof many tumultuous and riotous meetings and outrages have been by them frequently had and committed—not only on their masters but also on their fellow-labourers who refused to join with them in such their practices—by breaking into houses, spoiling of wool, and cutting and destroying the pieces in the looms and the utensils of trade.' On their side the weavers set forth 'the great hardships they labour under from their masters by paying their wages in goods and setting extravagant prices on such goods.' Parliament appointed a committee to hold an inquiry. One witness deposed that the weavers had many clubs in the west of England where they made by-laws constituting officers, arranging places of meeting at which 'ensigns and flags' were openly displayed, fixing wages, and making allowances to unemployed workmen on travel. Another affirmed that parties of weavers went round the weavers' homes demanding money for the support of those committed to prison in the recent riots; and that any who did not pay their contributions or worked at lower rates than others were liable to have their looms 'cut' and their work stolen.

As a result of the representations made by the employers, an act was passed in 1726 which forbade under penalty of imprisonment all combinations of weavers and wool-combers formed with the object of regulating the industry and improving the conditions of labour; and breach of contract, quitting an employer's service before the expiration of the period for which the workman had been hired, was made a criminal offence. The act was intended by its authors to stifle the trade union movement at its birth: nevertheless it was not a purely one-sided measure since it contained provisions for the 'better payment of wages.' While the state refused to recognize the right of working men to combine together for the protection and advancement of their economic interests, it still accepted in principle at least the duty of safeguarding the economic welfare of the industrial masses. The real criticism against the act of 1726 is that it did not affect equally both sections of the industrial community. The employers remained free to exercise a right which was refused to working men; and the clothiers (as Adam Smith expressly tells us) entered into combinations 'always conducted with the utmost silence and secrecy,' in order to maintain their common interests.

· The wool-combers were also organized in unions, and their relations with the employers were far from friendly. A worsted manufacturer of Nottinghamshire declared in 1794 that 'the manufacturers are entirely at the mercy of their combers and must pay them whatever wages they demand, particularly when trade is in a flourishing state, insomuch that if a manufacturer displeases one wool-comber all the others either quit his service entirely or until he appeases the offended member, and no other wool-comber will work for him so long as he continues under the displeasure of any of the members of their society.'

The organization of the cloth-finishers first emerges into prominence at the end of the eighteenth century; and an interesting account of the Yorkshire union, the Croppers' Society—corresponding to the Cloth-Dressers' Society in the west of England—is given in the *Report on the State of the Woollen Manufacture* (1806). 'It appears that there has existed for some time an institution or society among the woollen manufacturers consisting chiefly of cloth-workers. In each of the principal manufacturing towns there appears to be a society composed of deputies chosen from the several shops of workmen; from each of which town societies one or more deputies are chosen to form what is called the central committee, which meets as occasion requires at some place suitable to the local convenience of all parties. The powers of the central committee appear to pervade the whole institution; and any determination or measure it may adopt may be communicated with ease throughout the whole body of manufacturers. Every workman on his becoming a member of the society receives a certain card or ticket on which is an emblematical engraving, the same both in the north and the west of England, that by producing his ticket he may at once show he belongs to the society. The same rules and regulations appear to be in force throughout the whole district; and there is the utmost reason to believe that no cloth-worker would be suffered to carry on his trade otherwise than in solitude who should refuse to submit to the obligations and rules of the society. A stated weekly contribution, greater or less according to existing circumstances, is required from every member and of course the sum raised in this way may be and in fact has been very considerable. It appears that from the fund liberal weekly allowances have been made to whole shops of workmen who have turned out, as it is called—*i.e.* who have illegally combined to quit the service of some particular master who has become obnoxious to them, and thereby to force him into a compliance with their terms. It likewise appears that the society —which by embracing only the workmen in the woollen manufacture throughout so large a district must both from its numbers and its pecuniary resources have become a very powerful body—had formed a sort of confederacy, cemented as it appears by mutual contributions and payments, with various other classes of artificers nowise connected with the woollen trade; and that these connections and the effects of them were not confined to the clothing district but that they extended to various parts of England, and (your committee have reason to believe) into Scotland also.' The objects of this combination among cloth-finishers were fourfold: to raise wages, prescribe the age at which apprentices should be taken, regulate the number of apprentices in accordance with the number of journeymen, and resist the introduction of machinery.

CHAPTER SEVEN

Processes and Inventions

IN ORDER TO UNDERSTAND the inventions which revolutionized the woollen and worsted industries, we must gain some notion of the main technical processes involved in the preparation and manufacture of cloth. The different stages of cloth-making are described in a poem printed in 1641:[1]

> As first, the Parter that doth neatly cull
> The finer from the coarser sort of wool.
> The Dyer then in order next doth stand
> With sweating brow and a laborious hand.
> With oil they then asperge it, which being done,
> The careful hands of Mixers round it run.
> The Stock-carder his arms doth hard employ
> (Remembering Friday is our Market Day).
> Then Knee-carder doth (without control)
> Quickly convert it to a lesser roll.
> Which done, the Spinster doth in hand it take
> And of two hundred rolls one thread doth make.
> The Weaver next doth warp and weave the chain
> Whilst Puss his cat stands mewing for a skein.
> But he laborious with his hands and heels
> Forgets his cat and cries: Come boy with quills.
> Being fill'd the Brayer doth it mundify
> From oil and dirt that in the same doth lie.
> The Burler then (yea thousands in this place)
> The thick-set weed with nimble hand doth chase.
> The Fuller then close by his stock doth stand
> And will not once shake Morpheus by the hand.
> The Rower next his arms lifts up on high.
> And near him sings the Shearman merrily.

[1] R. Watts, *The Young Man's Looking Glass.*

The Drawer, last, that many faults doth hide
(Whom merchant nor the weaver can abide).
Yet he is one in most cloths stops more holes
Than there be stairs to the top of Paul's.

The first process was wool-sorting. 'The perfect and principal
ground of cloth-making,' declared a statute of 1554, 'is the true
sorting of wools.' The long wool had to be divided from the
short wool, and the different qualities—there might be more
than a dozen 'sorts' in a single fleece—carefully separated.

In the same fleece diversity of wool
Grows intermingled, and excites the care
Of curious skill to sort the sev'ral kinds.
    Nimbly with habitual speed
They sever lock from lock, and long and short
And soft and rigid pile in sev'ral heaps.[1]

After being sorted the wool was scoured to dissolve the grease.
The operation was done in a stream. The short wool was put
in baskets, and the water was 'drained through the baskets
leaving the wool behind, which was dried in lofts or in the sun.
The long wool was washed with two poles, having crooks at one
end, which were twisted reverse ways squeezing the water out
like wringing a towel.' The wool had to be cleansed from
miscellaneous impurities; in unwashed wool foreign matter
made up a very considerable part of the weight.[2] Also the farmers often branded the sheep with pitch and tar; this was
detrimental to the wool which also suffered from excessive
marking. The manufacturers were therefore obliged to waste an
appreciable quantity of wool in clipping off the damaged parts.
Another abuse was the fraudulent winding of wool, stigmatised
as 'a crime of ancient date.' As early as 1532 it was enacted
'that no person should wind within any fleece clay, lead, stones,
tail, deceitful locks, cotts, eals, comber, lamb's wool or any
other thing whereby the fleece might be more weighty to the
deceit and loss of the buyer.' In some parcels of wool one-
fifteenth of the weight was lost owing to malpractices in marking

[1] Dyer, *The Fleece* (1757).
[2] See Part I.

and winding; and in the middle of the eighteenth century
complaints were presented to Parliament from sixty centres of
the cloth trade. The cause of the growers was taken up by John
Smith, the author of *Memoirs of Wool*, who defended them from
the accusations of the manufacturers 'the inveterate antagonists
to wool growers for ages and centuries.'

When the wool was dry[1] it was beaten with rods to free it
from dust, an operation known as willeying. It was then picked
to remove any refuse which had escaped the rods. After
these operations of sorting and cleansing, the wool was in a condition to undergo the preliminary processes of manufacturing—
namely carding or combing.[2]

Wool textiles were divided into two main branches—the
woollen branch or manufacture of short carded wool; and
the worsted branch or manufacture of long combed wool.[3] The
term cloth was used where both warp and weft were spun from
carded wool, while the term stuff denoted that warp and weft
were spun from combed wool. A third category, serge, was
created by the mixture of carded and combed wool—the weft
being carded yarn and the warp combed yarn. These 'three
fundamental sorts,' as they were called, were subdivided into
a great number of others 'according to certain qualities added
to them and different ways of working.' Thus combed wool,
as we learn from a list given to Parliament in 1794, was
used in the manufacture (among others) of sagathies, duroy,
estamanes, shalloons, poplins, lastings, callimanco, bombazine, stuff-damask, camlets, crapes, russells, druggets, sanfords
and baize.

The short wool, as already stated, was carded and the
long wool combed. The purpose of carding was to disintegrate
the locks of wool, and straighten out and interlace the fibres.
It was done by means of hand-cards which resembled hand-
brushes in shape, the backs being made of stout card or wood
twelve inches long and five inches wide, and the fronts being

[1] Or even before it was washed.
[2] For the processes of scribbling and slubbing, see Chapter Eight.
[3] The historic difference between woollens and worsteds was that the latter
underwent the combing process. Short carded wool can now be used in the
worsted manufacture owing to improvements in combing machinery.

fitted with short pieces of wire (instead of bristles) set in a leather cover. The wool was spread in small quantities upon one of the cards, and brushed and combed with the other until all the fibres were disentangled from the locks and crossed in every direction, after which it was stripped off the card in soft fleecy rolls termed slivers. Originally the cards were held one in each hand; but subsequently one of the cards was made a fixture, and its size was also increased so that a greater quantity of wool could be spread on it. A later improvement was to suspend the card from the ceiling, which relieved the operator from bearing its weight. The new type of cards bore the name of stock cards. The sliver was converted into a thick coarse thread called roving, and the rovings were then spun into a fine twisted thread termed yarn. The method of roving was analogous to that of spinning, and both involved the use of the same instrument: a description of spinning will therefore serve as a description of roving. We must first, however, say a word about the process which corresponded to carding in the worsted industry—namely, wool-combing.

Three implements were employed in wool-combing—a pair of combs, a post to which one of the combs was fixed, and a comb-pot or small stove for heating the teeth of the combs. The comb was a piece of wood shaped like the letter T. The perpendicular part served as the handle; while the horizontal part or head, which usually measured three inches in width, contained long pointed teeth. The teeth were 'finely tapered, made of well-tempered steel, and generally arranged in three rows about thirty in each and placed nearly at right angles to every part of the wood.' The wool was hung upon the teeth of the comb affixed to the post 'in such a manner as to project over the front of the head; when sufficiently filled and firmly fixed, another comb of the same kind was drawn through the wool so as to unravel and lay each hair of it smooth and even.' The comb not only served to lay the fibres parallel with each other but also to separate the long wool (the top) from the wool of shorter staple (the noil). The work of the wool-combers was both unpleasant and unhealthy. According to an account written in 1845, 'the wool-combers assort the wool chiefly in

I

an apartment of their own dwelling. The work is done over a fire of charcoal which sends forth volumes of carbonic acid gas, and the workpeople are obliged to keep their windows open in all weathers to prevent or to mitigate the evil effects of the gas. They are roasted to perspiration on one side, and have often a current of cold air rushing upon them from the window. They look pale and cadaverous and are short-lived, few reaching fifty years of age.' The discontent which prevailed among them may be attributed in part to the 'harassing and enfeebling nature of their employment and their ill-ventilated and unhealthy dwellings.' It was, indeed, an argument in favour of machinery that the hand-comber 'confined to noisome abodes [was] enervated by the heat and effluvium of charcoal fires.'

The original method of spinning—the word means to draw out and twist the fibres of wool so as to form a continuous thread —was the distaff (or rock) and spindle. The distaff was a cleft staff about a yard long with a forked top on which a fleece of wool, called the lint or tow, was loosely wound. It was held under the left arm or sometimes carried in the girdle of the spinner in order to give freedom to the hands. The procedure was to draw a continuous lock of wool from the fleece through the fingers of the left hand, and twist it between the forefinger and thumb of the right with the aid of a pendent spindle. The latter was a slender rod constructed of reed or other light wood and measuring eight to twelve inches in length. An incision was made at the top for attaching the thread to the spindle, and as the spindle was perpetually revolving it served to draw out and produce a more finely twisted thread. The lower end of the spindle was inserted in a whorl—a ring or weight usually made of stone but sometimes of metal or wood—with a hole bored through the centre to admit the spindle. The main object of the whorl was to act as a flywheel to the whirling spindle, keeping it steady by its weight and making it revolve uniformly. It also served a subsidiary purpose in preventing 'the thread from becoming unravelled by shuffling down from the centre to the end.' Another form of spindle was 'an elongated cone of wood, the lower end being the thicker and acting as the weight;' here no whorl was needed to serve as a flywheel. As the spinner gradually lengthened the thread with her fingers, the spindle touched the ground and a length was said to be spun. The thread was then wound upon the spindle, another portion of the tow was attached to the top of the spindle, and the spinner set to work upon a fresh length. This mode of spinning, which was prevalent in ancient times, is thus described by Catullus:

> The loaded distaff, in the left hand placed,
> With spongy coils of snow-white wool was graced;
> From these the right hand lengthening fibres drew,
> Which into thread 'neath nimble fingers grew.

The discovery of whorls in the Pictish towers (brochs) affords evidence of the distaff and spindle in these islands in the remotest times. Their survival in the eighteenth century is indicated in Dyer's poem *The Fleece* (1757):

> Many yet adhere
> To th' ancient distaff, at the bosom fix'd,
> Casting the whirling spindle as they walk.

And more than a hundred years later they were still being used.

The distaff and spindle were eventually superseded by the spinning-wheel (or hand-wheel), which was erroneously supposed to have been introduced into England by an Italian in the sixteenth century but was really known in this country at least as early as the fourteenth century.[1] The purpose of the spinning-wheel was to give motion to the spindle by means of a revolving wheel. Instead of being suspended by the thread, the spindle was 'mounted in a frame and turned by a belt passing over a large wheel.' The following description was written in the early nineteenth century. 'In spinning with the hand-wheel the roving was taken fast hold of betwixt the left forefinger and thumb at six inches distance from the spindle. The wheel, which by a band gave motion to the spindle, was then turned with the right hand, and at the same time the left hand—holding the roving fast as before mentioned—was

---

[1] It is mentioned in the *Records of Nottingham*.

drawn back about half a yard. The roving was thus drawn out into weft,[1] the necessary twist was then given by a few turns of the wheel, and finally the weft was wound upon the spindle.' Adam Smith asserts that the exchange of the distaff and spindle for the spinning-wheel enabled a spinner to perform more than double the quantity of work with the same quantity of labour. At first the wheel was turned by one hand, and the thread twisted and drawn out by the other; subsequently the wheel was turned by a treadle and crank which the spinner worked with her foot. This left the spinner free to employ both her hands in spinning the thread. 'In my memory,' stated the writer of a treatise on *Silk, Wool, Worsted, Cotton, and Thread* (1779), 'wool was spun on the long wheel only, which was tedious and irregular, the wheel being at least five feet perpendicular with one spindle. This wheel was turned by a peg with the right hand, and the wool spun from the left by the hand being extended as the wheel was turned. The next invention was a one-handed wheel—so-called from its motion being continued with one hand, and the yarn spun with the other and twisted with a spindle and flyer. In 1750 a wheel was invented to spin with both hands, turned with the feet.'[2]

Weaving has been defined as the art by which threads are crossed and interlaced. We may expand the definition by saying that a piece of cloth is made up of longitudinal threads laid parallel to each other and intersected by transverse threads. The longitudinal threads constitute the warp or chain, the transverse threads the weft or woof.[3] The process of weaving consists in inserting the threads of the weft between the alternate threads of the warp.

The first task of the weaver was to arrange the warp in order on the loom. This was termed looming; and unless the warp was 'put square' (fixed properly) on the loom, every thread at an equal tension, the texture of the cloth would be uneven. The loom was framed like an oblong box, four upright posts being joined together by two long and two short posts. At one end of

---

[1] *I.e.* thread.
[2] For the defects of hand-spinning, see above Chapter Five.
[3] The weft was also called abb and shute.

the loom was the warp beam, at the other end the cloth beam. The warp threads were laid parallel to each other extending lengthwise across the loom from one beam to the other, and as the cloth was woven it was wound upon the cloth beam and fresh warp was paid out by the warp beam. In the middle of the loom the warp passed through two sets of healds. The latter were small parallel cords or wires, stretched vertically between two horizontal bars, each cord having a loop or eye for the admission of a single thread of the warp. The even threads of the warp passed through the loops of one leaf[1] or set of healds, the odd threads through the loops of the other leaf. There were thus two series of warp threads, the even and the odd, the former controlled by the first set of healds and the latter by the second set. The healds were worked by two treadles; and when one treadle was depressed by the foot, it lifted the other treadle as well as the set of healds connected with it. The contrivance enabled the weaver to raise alternately one section of the threads of the warp for the passage of the weft. The warp threads were then inserted in the batten or sley, a movable wooden frame designed on the principle of a comb with a large number of dents through each of which several threads of the warp were drawn to keep them in position.

When the warp was prepared in the manner we have described, the weaver seated himself at the loom and with his foot depressed the right treadle. This raised the left treadle, and (as explained above) made an opening or shed in the warp. Through the shed he now swiftly threw the shuttle—a piece of wood tapering to a point at each end and containing a cavity or chamber for the reception of the bobbin or quill, a small reed pipe on which was wound a quantity of weft. As the shuttle shot across the warp from the right side of the loom to the left, the weft unrolled itself from the bobbin and escaped through a small hole or eye in the side of the shuttle. The weft thread was then beaten home and packed close by the batten against the stretch of cloth already produced by former throws (picks as they were called) of the shuttle. The left treadle was in its turn depressed; this caused the right treadle to rise and with it the

[1] A leaf, the name given to a set of healds, was also termed gear.

alternate series of warp threads, forming another shed for the passage of the shuttle from the left side to the right.

> And now he strains the warp
> Along the garden-walk or highway side,
> Smoothing each thread; now fits it to the loom
> And sits before the work; from hand to hand
> The thready shuttle glides along the lines;
> And ever and anon, to firm the work,
> Against the web is driv'n the noisy frame
> .That o'er the level rushes like a surge.

The art of weaving, apart from the laborious task of fixing the warp on the loom, thus involved three distinct operations— opening alternate sheds in the warp by means of the treadles; casting the shuttle through each shed when opened; and driving home the weft threads with the batten. The swiftness of the shuttle became proverbial:

> My days are swifter than a weaver's shuttle.

A single weaver was able to work a narrow loom, throwing the shuttle with one hand and catching it with the other; but two weavers were needed for the broad loom, one at each end to receive and return the shuttle thrown by his partner.

Hand-loom weaving, as a writer pointed out in 1836, 'is not easy labour; the position in which the weaver sits is not the best for muscular exertion as he has no firm support for his feet, which are alternately raised and depressed in working the treadles. He has thus to depend for a fulcrum chiefly on the muscles of his back which are kept in constant and vigorous action, while one order of muscles is employed with little power of variation in moving the shuttle and [batten]. These processes, when carried on for many successive hours, are very wearying and the exertion required becomes after a while laborious. The weaver who worked hard, therefore, actually toiled—a condition widely different from that of the steam-loom weaver.' Another criticism of hand-loom weaving is that the most experienced workers rarely wove cloth uniform in texture; they could not throw the shuttle nor drive home the batten, from beginning to end, with the even force and mechanical precision of a power-loom; and a weaker or stronger blow at once affected the texture. Nor could a hand-loom weaver work at the speed of a steam-loom, which was able to make many more times the number of picks per minute. The power-loom not only reproduced the human movements but it accelerated their speed, and combined with them an endurance that was inexhaustible.

Weaving was not the final process in cloth-making, for as Langland wrote:

Cloth that cometh fro the weaving is naught comely to wear
Till it is fulled under foot or in fulling stocks,
Washen well with water, and with teasles scratched,
Tucked and tented, and under tailor's hand.

After the cloth was woven it was scoured in order to get rid of the oil used in scribbling and of the size with which the warp was dressed; it was burled, that is, the knots and extraneous particles in the cloth were picked out; and (in the case of woollen cloth only)[1] it was fulled.

A normal difference between woollen and worsted fabrics was that the former were thickened and felted with the result that the fibres, instead of lying parallel with each other, were inextricably interlaced and the woven pattern of the cloth frequently ceased to be visible. The process of felting is known as fulling: the cloth was soaped and beaten in a damp state with heavy wooden hammers so as to make it warmer, opaque and more durable. The primitive method of fulling consisted in trampling the cloth underfoot until it was sufficiently shrunk —a piece of cloth often shrank up to two-thirds of its original length and about half its original width. Accordingly the fuller was sometimes called a walker. The first improvement in the art of fulling was to substitute a sitting posture for an erect one, thereby enabling the operation to be performed with greater rapidity and ease. Thomas Pennant, who visited the north of Scotland in 1774 and came across a survival of the ancient mode of fulling with hand and

---

[1] Some worsteds are now lightly milled (*i.e.* fulled).

foot in the Isle of Skye, gives the following interesting description of it: 'On my return am entertained with a rehearsal, I may call it, of the Luaghad or walking of cloth, a substitute for the fulling mill; twelve or fourteen women divided into equal numbers sit down on each side of a long board ribbed lengthways, placing the cloth on it; first they begin to work it backwards and forwards with their hands, singing at the same time as at the Quern;[1] when they have tired their hands every female uses her feet for the same purpose, and six or seven pairs of naked feet are in the most violent agitation working one against the other; as by this time they grow very earnest in their labours the fury of the song rises; at length it arrives to such a pitch that without breach of charity you would imagine a troop of female demoniacs to have been assembled. They sing in the same manner when they are cutting down the corn, when thirty or forty join in chorus. The subjects of the songs at the Luaghad, the Quern and on this occasion are sometimes love, sometimes panegyric, often a rehearsal of the deeds of ancient heroes, but all the tunes slow and melancholy.' Over a century later another writer describes 'a picturesque sight' in the Highlands. 'A dozen or more Highland lassies sit round in two rows facing each other. The web of cloth is passed round in a damp state, each one pressing and pitching it with a dash to her next neighbour.' The process is slow and tedious but the time is beguiled with song, each taking up the verse in turn and all joining in the chorus. 'Should a member of the male sex be found prowling nearby he is—if caught—unceremoniously thrust into the centre of the circle and tossed with the web till, bruised with the rough usage and blackened with the dye, he is glad to make his escape from the hands of the furies.'

The use of fulling mills in place of 'hand and foot' dates from very early times; they afford apparently the oldest example of the application of motive-power to the textile industries. The fullery consisted of wooden hammers or shafts—hinged to an upright post and worked by water-power—and hollow vessels known as stocks or fuller's pots, which held the cloth as it was

[1] *I.e.* mill-grinding.

pounded by the strokes of the hammers. Dyer's account of the fulling mill runs:

> Next from the slacken'd beam the woof unroll'd,
> Near some clear sliding river Aire or Stroud,
> Is by the noisy fulling mill receiv'd;
> Where tumbling waters turn enormous wheels,
> And hammers rising and descending learn
> To imitate the industry of man.

The employment of water mills for fulling aroused great opposition. As early as 1298 London prohibited fulling at the mills instead of 'by might and strength of man and that is with hand and foot.' The prohibition was removed in 1417 on the ground that water mills involved less cost and were equally serviceable, but it was revived twenty years later. The antagonism to machinery driven by power was doubtless one of the main reasons for the delay in its introduction into industry. In 1485, for example, the owner of a fulling mill in the Stroud Valley was attacked by a crowd of 'malefactors *vi et armis*— viz. with swords, sticks, bows and arrows, scythes, jakkes, armour etc.—with intent to murder him so that he was many times affrighted and disturbed.' The opposition to the fulling mill eventually died down yet another grievance was voiced at Pontefract in 1739. Complaint was made to the justices that 'it is, and for many years last past hath been, a common practice to mill narrow cloth upon sundays; and that the cloth-makers are now arrived to such a scandalous and shocking degree of prophaning the sabbath this way, that they even contrive to bring more cloths to be milled upon sunday than any other day. Whereby both masters and servants are guilty of a public neglect of the holy duties of the day, and by certain consequence are insensibly drawn into the commission of all manner of sin and wickedness to the great displeasure of Almighty God, the scandal of the kingdom, the evil example of their neighbours, and the breach of all laws both divine and human.'

When the cloth had been fulled it was stretched on tenters in the open air to dry. Next it was dressed or finished. The finishing process involved two operations—one was rowing, that is, drawing out the loose fibres from the cloth with teasles[1] so as to raise a nap on the surface; the other was shearing, that is, cropping the nap as closely as possible so as to impart a smooth appearance to the surface. The cloth now passed into the hands of the drawer who repaired any blemishes; and then it was pressed between heated plates and packed for the market.

Dyeing was a separate process in itself. Sometimes the wool was dyed after it was washed but before it was woven. Wool-dyed cloth was termed medley cloth; it was made out of the same material as white cloth though its wool was dyed before weaving. In the west country most Wiltshire cloth was said to be dyed in the wool, while Gloucestershire cloth was chiefly dyed in the piece after being woven. According to Luccock, an authority on wool, the methods of dyeing were distinctly primitive in Yorkshire. He wrote (1805): 'But indeed what can we expect but faint, muddy and uncertain colours where wool is dyed—as is too much the custom in Yorkshire—without being scoured, in pans unwashed, and with materials mixed together upon a floor unswept where a little before perhaps have been mixed ingredients calculated to produce a totally different tint?'

Of the inventions, whose history we have now to relate, the fly shuttle and the carding machine were first introduced into the woollen industry; the combing machine was confined to the worsted industry; spinning by rollers was intended both for wool and cotton textiles; and the power-loom was designed for cotton and subsequently applied to wool.

John Kay, the inventor of the fly shuttle, was born in 1704 at Walmersley near Bury in Lancashire. In 1733 he patented an invention which enabled one weaver to do the work of two and ushered in an era of revolutionary changes in the organiza-tion and distribution of the textile industries. The main feature of Kay's device was the new mode of casting the shuttle. The batten was flanked on each side by a shuttle race-board along

[1] A teasle is a plant with prickly leaves.

which the shuttle ran on wheels. The boards were connected by means of a cord with a lever or picking peg held in the right hand. A jerk of the picking peg gave the necessary impetus to the shuttle which was driven to and fro across the warp mechanically without being thrown by the weaver's hands, one of which was thus left entirely free to work the batten and beat together the weft threads. The speed at which the shuttle could now be thrown gained for the new contrivance the name of fly shuttle. Robert Kay, a son of John Kay, afterwards invented the drop box which made it possible to use a variety of shuttles, each containing a different coloured weft. The invention of the fly shuttle, or spring loom, enabled a weaver to dispense with assistance in weaving broadcloth; he ceased to be dependent on a journeyman whose irregular habits arising from idleness, intemperance or sickness had often hindered his work. Nevertheless hand-loom weaving is not merely a matter of throwing a shuttle; it involves the laborious task of binding the warp threads on the loom and repairing broken threads. A weaver had to do all this on the spring loom single-handed, and some maintained that the work could not be done in the same time. The fly shuttle certainly increased the production of cloth since one operative now sufficed to work a loom, and he was able to earn more money. It also effected an improvement in his health; he sat upright instead of having to lean forward and so was less subject to breast disorders. Yet the work was apparently more strenuous and the common or double-handed loom still had its use for older men.[1]

It has been said that Kay's invention called forth 'that opposition of the working classes to the abridgement of processes of labour which was so conspicuous a fact for nearly a century afterwards in British industry.' Actually from very early times textile workers had displayed a resolute antagonism to 'the abridgement of processes of labour.' They fought strenuously against the use of fulling and gig mills in the finishing processes

[1] When Kay's fly shuttle was introduced into the north of Ireland the new process of weaving attracted large crowds, and one woman 'was enthusiastic in her admiration of it. Clapping her hands she exclaimed in Scoto-Hibernic phraseology: "Weel, weel! the warks o' God's wondtherful but the contrivance o' man bates Him at last!" '

of the cloth industry; and their hostility to Kay and the long line of inventors who succeeded him sprang from a traditional dislike of innovations, coupled with a deep-rooted fear that machinery would take from them their means of livelihood. In the case of inventions like the fly shuttle the folly of resisting improvements was soon rendered manifest, for the hand-loom weavers were the first to benefit by changes which gave them a more perfect command over their instruments. Kay's ill-fated career is a melancholy illustration of the evil destiny which has pursued so many of the English inventors; their lives have frequently been a sequence of disappointments, sometimes relieved by transitory gleams of success but more often shrouded in obscurity and gloom. The weavers of Colchester, where Kay lived, opposed the introduction of the fly shuttle. Their enmity drove him to the north of England and he settled in Leeds. Here he found himself in conflict with the West Riding clothiers, who adopted his invention yet declined to pay for it. In order to protect themselves in this mean and dishonest conduct they even established an association under the name of 'The Shuttle Club,' which bore the costs of the lawsuits brought by the inventor in defence of his rights. Abandoning the country which had given so rude a welcome to his inventive talent Kay went into exile abroad. The French government awarded him a pension in return for his making shuttles, and he died in France about the age of seventy-five.

Who first conceived the idea of automatic spinning? The claims of four men have been widely canvassed—Lewis Paul, John Wyatt, Richard Arkwright, and Thomas Highs. The problem has never been satisfactorily solved though one fundamental fact is beyond all reasonable dispute. The mode of spinning by rollers was undoubtedly known a generation before Arkwright, with whose name the invention is commonly associated, set up his first machine in the house of a Preston schoolmaster. The date of its invention is 1738, for in that year a patent was taken out in the name of Lewis Paul, and the specification explaining the nature and scope of the machine anticipates the vital principles of the water-frame. It states that the sliver 'is put between a pair of rollers [and], being turned round by their motion, draws in the raw mass of wool or cotton to be spun in proportion to the velocity of such rollers. A succession of other rollers, moving proportionately faster than the rest, draw the rope, thread, or sliver, into any degree of fineness that may be required.' In addition 'the bobbin, spole or quill—upon which the thread is spun—is so contrived as to draw faster than the first rollers give and in such proportion as the sliver is proposed to be diminished.' The description of the machine which bears Paul's name demonstrates that Arkwright, whatever his other merits, was not the original inventor of the mode of spinning by rollers.

The career of Lewis Paul, the reputed inventor of the first English machine on which thread was ever spun without the aid of human fingers, is obscure. He was the son of a French refugee who settled in our country during an era of religious persecution in France. In his enterprises Paul associated himself with a skilled mechanic, John Wyatt, and the latter has been credited with the real authorship of the invention. This was the expressed belief of Wyatt's descendants, and it was shared by one of the earliest investigators into the history of the textile inventions. 'The merit of conceiving the principle of spinning by rollers,' according to Edward Baines, 'is the glory of Wyatt.' The letters and papers of Paul and Wyatt have come to light; and they appear to show that the merit really belongs to Paul, while Wyatt was the mechanic who carried out his ideas. A memorandum in the handwriting of John Wyatt, discovered among his papers, has established the point. 'Thoughts originally Mr. Paul's—1. The joining of the rolls. 2. Their passing through cylinders. 3. The calculation of the wheels, by which means the bobbin draws faster than those cylinders. This I presume was picked up somewhere before I knew him.' Wyatt only claimed for himself various mechanical improvements which his experience as a trained mechanic would enable him to introduce into Paul's machine. Another piece of evidence is that Paul, who owed Wyatt over £800, undertook to give his assistant the plan which he himself was using for 'erecting, making and perfecting proper machines or engines and spindles for the spinning of wool or cotton.' Wyatt also received the right to set up three hundred spindles for the spinning of wool or cotton 'according to the new invention of Lewis Paul,' and the contract contains a significant passage: 'The said Lewis Paul shall and will give unto the said John Wyatt such further instructions for the erecting, making and perfecting of the machines or engines and spindles as shall be requisite and needful for the effectual working and management of the same.' This language seems to admit only of one conclusion—that Paul, not Wyatt, was the inventor of the machine which was the subject of the contract.

A mill was erected at Birmingham (1738–1743), and another was started at Northampton with money furnished by Cave the editor of *The Gentleman's Magazine*. Dyer, in his poem *The Fleece* (1757), alludes to Paul's invention in the following terms:

> We next are shown
> A circular machine of new design
> In conic shape: it draws and spins a thread
> Without the tedious toil of needless hands.
> A wheel, invisible, beneath the floor
> To ev'ry member of th' harmonious frame
> Gives necessary motion. One, intent,
> O'erlooks the work: the carded wool, he says,
> Is smoothly lapp'd around those cylinders,
> Which gently turning yield it to yon cirque
> Of upright spindles, which with rapid whirl
> Spin out in long extent an even twine.

The enterprise proved a failure in both places. Paul was short of capital, and his letters to Wyatt reveal the straits to which he was often reduced in his desperate efforts to raise the necessary funds. Even Wyatt himself saw for a time the inside of a debtors' prison. Another reason for Paul's inability to reap the fruits of his inventive genius, and to achieve the commercial success which afterwards attended Arkwright's own efforts in the same field, was doubtless the imperfect nature of his machine. Although the principle was identical in both cases, Paul's machine was inferior to his successor's in point of construction. The subsequent fate of Paul's invention has given rise to much speculation. The problem is whether it entirely lapsed or whether it was revived in the next generation. The claims of two inventors have been upheld—Richard Arkwright and Thomas Highs a reed-maker of Leigh. In the absence of authentic information we must content ourselves with stating the various alternatives, one of which must contain the solution of the problem. It is possible that the knowledge of Paul's invention came to the ears of either Arkwright or Highs, and that one or the other constructed a machine on its principles; and it is possible, again, that one of them conceived the idea of roller spinning independently—rediscovering a secret which had been forgotten. However these hypotheses are in the main pure conjecture; one thing alone is certain; the successful application of automatic spinning was the work of Arkwright.

Richard Arkwright, the most prominent figure in the history of the textile industries, was born at Preston in 1732 the youngest of thirteen children. He was apprenticed to a barber and settled in Bolton where he obtained some reputation for his skill as a wig-maker. He had no knowledge of mechanics and no practical acquaintance with industrial processes, but he had a quick alert mind, an insatiable curiosity and a genius for assimilating and developing the ideas of others. He was drawn irresistibly to mechanical experiments, and chance threw him about the year 1767 in the path of a clock-maker Kay[1] whom he employed to construct his apparatus. Whether or not his discovery of the basic principles of Paul's invention was the fruit of his own ingenuity, he came into possession of the secret which was destined to revolutionize the textile industries and create the factory system.

Arkwright had now reached the first milestone along the road which was to lead him to fame and fortune; yet to achieve his goal took him many years of unwearied application and devoted labour. In 1769 he took out a patent for his machine, and this event marked the second milestone in his career. One of his chief difficulties arose from the infringement of his patent rights. Every successful inventor is liable to be the victim of unscrupulous attempts to rob him of the fruits of his enterprise,

[1] Not to be confused with the inventor of the fly shuttle.

and Arkwright was no exception to the rule. He was driven to defend himself in a court of law (1785) and obtained judgment in his favour. The verdict caused a great sensation among his fellow-manufacturers who had installed his machinery in their factories without taking the precaution of securing Arkwright's permission, and they made a vigorous effort to obtain a reversal of the judgment. A few months later a fresh trial was held. Highs and Kay came forward to swear that Arkwright was not the inventor of the machines which were patented in his name. The decisive factor, however, was Arkwright's own fatal admission that the specification of his patent was obscure. Every patentee is required by law to draw up a specification 'particularly describing and ascertaining the nature of his invention and in what manner the same is to be performed,' in order that anyone may know how to use the patent when the copyright has expired. The specification in which Arkwright described his machines was admittedly obscure. He endeavoured to justify his action on the ground that he desired to preserve his secret from foreigners, though the general opinion was that he was more concerned to protect it from his fellow-countrymen. A verdict was given for the defendants; as a result the patent was cancelled, and the water-frame together with the carding machine became the common property of the manufacturing world. In spite of the failure to drive his competitors from the field which his enterprise had opened up, Arkwright achieved both fame and fortune. He not only reaped a rich harvest by the sale of his machines before his patent rights were cancelled, but he entered into several partnerships which gave him a controlling interest in numerous concerns where his unrivalled skill in business, shrewd judgment and remarkable faculty for organization enjoyed abundant scope.[1]

The leading feature of the water-frame was the use of rollers. The roving was inserted between a pair of rollers placed in a horizontal position one above the other. These rollers revolved in contact, and as they revolved they compressed and drew the roving from the bobbins. Another pair of rollers, which

[1] He was knighted in 1786 and died in 1792.

revolved five times as fast, received the roving from the first pair and their rapid revolutions reduced the thick roving into a fine thread. A twist was imparted to the thread by means of revolving spindles with which the roving was connected as it was drawn out of the second pair of rollers. The original machine erected by Arkwright at Nottingham was turned by horses. This proved an expensive method; and in order to utilize the resources of water-power Arkwright built a mill at Cromford in Derbyshire, which was worked by a water-wheel and was therefore called the water-frame.[1] The machine patented in 1769 was adapted only for converting the rovings into yarn; turning the sliver into rovings was still done by hand. A few years later (1775) Arkwright patented other inventions which enabled all the preliminary operations connected with spinning to be performed by machinery. He appears to have been the first to adapt the system of spinning by rollers to the process of roving, and for this purpose he invented the roving-frame built on the same principle as the water-frame. He was also the first apparently to introduce the drawing process—a kind of preparatory spinning intended to straighten the fibres and reduce the thickness of the roving when it had left the roving-frame.

Arkwright's most important achievement, after the water-frame, was a machine for carding by revolving cylinders in place of hand-cards. The idea was originally conceived both by Daniel Bourne and Lewis Paul. The machine which the latter invented was 'a horizontal cylinder covered with parallel rows of cards and turned by a handle. Under the cylinder was a concave frame lined internally with cards exactly fitting the lower half of the cylinder, so that when the handle was turned the cards of the cylinder and of the concave frame worked against each other and carded the wool,' the teeth of the cards on the cylinder and on the concave frame being in close contact. Paul's machine had three defects—there was no feeder and the wool was therefore applied to the cylinder by hand; the machine had to stop while the cardings were taken off by a movable comb; and a continuous carding was made

---

[1] With the application of steam it became known as the throstle.

K

by uniting short pieces with the hand. The first defect, the absence of a feeder, was removed as the result of an invention (1772) attributed to John Lees a Quaker of Manchester. This consisted of a 'perpetual revolving cloth' on which the material was spread and then fed to the cylinder. Other improvements were the work of Arkwright who brought to maturity the earlier ideas. He invented in 1775 the crank and comb: a 'plate of metal finely toothed at the edge like a comb which, being worked by a crank in a perpendicular direction, with slight but frequent strokes on the teeth of the card stripped off the [sliver] in a continuous filmy fleece.' A subsequent modification (1785) ensured a continuous carding by means of a comb joined to the cylinder and worked by a crank. The series of inventions associated with Arkwright's name thus enabled all the preliminary processes of the textile industries to be done by machinery instead of by hand. Henceforth wool could be carded, made into rovings and spun into yarn without the aid of human fingers.

Another great invention in spinning was the work of James Hargreaves a weaver of Standhill near Blackburn. The story runs that he 'received the original idea of his machine from seeing a one-thread wheel overturned upon the floor, when both wheel and spindle continued to revolve. The spindle was thus thrown from a horizontal into an upright position; and the thought seems to have struck him that if a number of spindles were placed upright and side by side, several threads might be spun at once.' This lucky inspiration gave birth in 1767 to the spinning jenny. The latter was a frame, in one part of which was set a row of eight rovings and in another part a row of eight spindles. The rovings were inserted between two flat pieces of wood, termed a clove, which opened and shut something like a parallel ruler and held the roving firm as in a clasp. A portion of each roving was connected with a spindle, and the clove travelled along the horizontal bars of the frame away from the spindles, drawing out the threads and reducing them to the proper fineness. At the same time the spinner turned a wheel which made the spindles revolve and twist the thread. The clove then returned towards the spindles in order to 'cop the weft'—that is, wind the spun yarn upon the spindles. The jenny is said to have taken its name from the fact that it performed the work of a female. In the woollen industry weft and warp were spun on the jenny, in contrast with cotton where apparently only weft was spun. The introduction of the jenny into the woollen manufacture followed closely upon its invention; and it does not seem correct to say that 'the great textile inventions did not extend to wool till much later, [and that] many years elapsed before the contrivance of Hargreaves was applied to spinning wool.' The number of spindles used in the jenny did not remain stationary. It was found possible for a spinner to take care of sixty or seventy and even as many as a hundred and twenty spindles at one time, and wages were trebled in consequence.

The water-frame and the jenny differed in several ways. The water-frame, although originally employed to reduce the rovings into yarn and not to turn the slivers into rovings, was subsequently adapted for this purpose; the jenny appears to have been restricted to the final process of spinning. Next the thread spun on the water-frame was harder—that is, more firmly twisted—and was suitable for warps; whereas the thread spun on the jenny was soft and therefore suitable for weft.[1] Lastly the jenny was an implement which the artisan was able to work in his own cottage with his own hands; but the water-frame was a machine which required more than human strength to give it motion. The difference between the jenny and the water-frame thus became the starting-point of a new economic order. The invention of the former was compatible with the retention of the domestic system of industry; the adoption of the latter brought in its train the establishment of the factory system.

After the water-frame and the jenny came the mule, which produced finer qualities of thread than either, and in the woollen industry displaced almost completely other modes of spinning.[2] The mule was the invention of Samuel Crompton.

---

[1] In the woollen industry also for warp.
[2] In the worsted industry yarns have continued to be spun mainly on some modification of the frame, namely, the cap, flyer, and ring.

Born at Firwood near Bolton in 1753 he was sixteen years of age when he learnt to spin upon the jenny, and barely twenty-one when he started to make improvements a task which occupied his leisure moments for the next five years. 'He was not a regular mechanic,' wrote his friend and biographer, Kennedy, 'and possessed only such tools as he purchased with his little earnings acquired by labour at the loom or jenny, and he had also to learn the use of those simple tools.' The new invention combined the principles both of Arkwright's and Hargreaves's machines:

> The forces of nature could no further go;
> To make a third she joined the former two.

The rovings as they were drawn out from the bobbins passed through the rollers to spindles placed on a spindle carriage. The leading feature of the mule, 'the great and important invention of Crompton' so Kennedy termed it, was the spindle carriage. Instead of the spindles being stationary (the method used in the case of the water-frame and the jenny), they were erected on a movable carriage or box which ran on wheels. As the rollers gave out the roving from the bobbins, the movable carriage—with the spindles in it rotating in order to twist the thread—receded from the rollers, drawing out and lengthening the thread. When the rollers had measured out a sufficient amount of the roving they ceased to revolve and held the roving fast, while the spindle carriage continued to recede to a distance of four to five feet. This stretched the thread to the requisite degree of fineness and imparted the necessary twist. To wind the thread upon the spindles the carriage was made to return to its original position.[1]

Many improvements were afterwards introduced into the mule as practical experience of the machine brought to light its deficiencies. 'The art of spinning on Crompton's machine,' wrote Kennedy, 'was tolerably well known from the circumstance of the high wages that could be obtained by those working on it, above the ordinary wages of other artisans such as shoemakers, joiners, hat-makers etc. who on that account

[1] The mule spun yarn for warp and weft.

left their previous employment; and to them might be applied the fable of the town in a state of siege. For, if in the course of their working the machine there was any little thing out of gear, each workman endeavoured to fill up the deficiency with some expedient suggested by his former trade; the smith suggested a piece of iron, the shoemaker a welt of leather, etc. all which had a good effect in improving the machine.' The most important improvement was the work of Richard Roberts, who invented an automatic or self-acting mule (1825). The year in which water-power was applied to the mule was 1790.

The introduction of machinery into the manufacture of yarn removed the defects of hand-spinning. For one thing machine-spun yarn was more uniform in quality; it was also firmer and stronger; the thread did not break so frequently. The weaver used only one-half the quantity of glue required for hand-spun yarn, which was 'tenderer' and needed more glue to hold it together. Another result of machinery was to liberate the weaver from his dependency upon the hand-spinner. He was now able to draw upon an unlimited supply of material for his work. The yarn famine was brought to an end and scarcity yielded place to abundance. It was estimated that a jenny could keep two looms at work, a mule perhaps ten looms, a throstle about the same number. In consequence the weaver was in a position to carry on his work more regularly throughout the year. The source upon which farmers had previously relied for labour in the harvest season (unemployed weavers) dried up; and it is significant to observe the complaints raised in some parts of the country that there was a general lack of labourers. A new problem was thus raised: instead of a shortage of spinners there was a shortage of weavers, and the invention of machinery in the weaving process seemed imperatively demanded. This was the achievement of Cartwright.

Edmund Cartwright, the inventor of the power-loom[1] and the combing machine, was born in 1743 in Nottinghamshire. A chance encounter 'with some gentlemen of Manchester'

[1] A loom worked by water-power was invented about 1678 by M. de Gennes, but it does not appear to have come into use.

embarked him on an inventor's career. The story can best be told in his own words: 'The conversation turned on Arkwright's spinning machinery. One of the company observed that as soon as Arkwright's patent expired so many mills would be erected, and so much cotton spun, that hands could never be found to weave it. To this observation I replied that Arkwright must then set his wits to work to invent a weaving machine. This brought on a conversation on the subject in which the Manchester gentlemen unanimously agreed that the thing was impracticable. Some little time afterwards a particular circumstance recalling this conversation to my mind it struck me that, as in plain weaving (according to the conception I then had of the business) there could only be three movements[1] which were to follow each other in succession, there would be little difficulty in producing and repeating them. Full of these ideas I immediately employed a carpenter and smith to carry them into effect. As soon as the machine was finished, I got a weaver to put in the warp which was of such materials as sail-cloth is usually made of. To my great delight a piece of cloth, such as it was, was the produce. As I had never before turned my thoughts to anything mechanical either in theory or in practice, nor had ever seen a loom at work or knew anything of its construction, you will readily suppose that my first loom was a most rude piece of machinery. The warp was placed perpendicularly, the reed fell with the weight of at least half a hundred-weight, and the springs which threw the shuttle were strong enough to have thrown a Congreve rocket. In short it required the strength of two powerful men to work the machine at a slow rate and only for a short time. Considering in my simplicity that I had accomplished all that was required, I then secured what I thought a most valuable property by a patent dated April 4, 1785. This being done I then condescended to see how other people wove, and you will guess my astonishment when I compared their easy modes of operations with mine. Availing myself however of what I then saw, I made a loom in its general principles nearly as they are now

---

[1] The three movements would be: opening the shed, throwing the shuttle, and beating the weft threads together.

made.[1] But it was not till the year 1787 that I completed my invention.'

Another outstanding achievement was the construction of a combing machine. Here Cartwright appears to have been guided by the same principle which underlies the mechanism of the power-loom: to imitate as closely as possible the movements of the hand yet to substitute a mechanical force for manual labour. The chief operations involved in hand-combing were threefold—filling the comb with wool, combing out the noil, and drawing off the sliver of top. These operations were reproduced in Cartwright's combing machine. The wool was passed through an oscillating frame, which was governed by a crank action, over and into the teeth of a circular comb revolving horizontally. 'As this [holding] comb slowly revolves it gradually becomes filled by a succession of tufts of wool lashed in from the frame; the fringe [or beard] of the tufts so held is carried round till it passes under the working comb which also traverses by a crank motion across the face of the [holding] comb, inserting the points of its teeth into the fringe and so—combing out the noil or refuse as the [holding] comb passes round—it brings the fringe in contact with the drawing-off rollers, which draw out the sliver of top leaving the noil behind in the chambers of the comb; the sliver is then carried forward through the conducting rollers into the receiving can below.' Cartwright's invention earned for him the title of the 'new Bishop Blaize'—the patron saint of the wool-combers—and his machine was known as 'Big Ben.' In honour of 'Big Ben' a song was composed by one of Cartwright's workmen:

Come all ye master combers and hear of new Big Ben;
He'll comb more wool in one day than fifty of your men
With their hand-combs and comb-pots and such
    old-fashion'd ways;
There'll be no more occasion for old Bishop Blaize.

The machine did not prove a satisfactory substitute for hand-combing. It was introduced into Bradford in 1794 where it was

[1] It differed from the hand-loom in the substitution of mechanical contrivances for the weaver's hands and feet.

worked by a horse, but the experiment was unsuccessful and was not repeated. Indeed, while the genius of Edmund Cartwright pointed the way, many decades were to elapse before the combing machine attained practical value and the requisite degree of perfection. Within a century of Cartwright's own invention the number of patents taken out in connexion with combing machines was nearly five hundred, and this affords remarkable proof of the industry and zeal with which a long line of inventors applied themselves to the problem. It is possible here to mention only the achievements of Heilmann, Donisthorpe, Lister, Holden, and Noble.

Josué Heilmann was born in Alsace in the year 1796. Smiles has related the story, for the truth of which we have independent authority, how he first conceived the idea enabling him to solve the problem which baffled the efforts of two generations. He was sitting by his hearth; and, 'meditating upon the hard fate of inventors and the misfortunes in which their families so often become involved, he found himself almost unconsciously watching his daughters combing their long hair and drawing it out at full length between their fingers. The thought suddenly struck him that if he could successfully imitate in a machine the process of combing out the longest hair, and forcing back the short by reversing the action of the comb, it might serve to extricate him from his difficulty.' Acting upon this inspiration he was able to devise a fundamental improvement in the mechanism of the combing machine. To understand the importance of Heilmann's achievement we must first grasp the defects of the existing methods of hand-combing and the machines built on its principles. 'In the process of washing the staples of wool become of course separated and the fibres crossed in all directions; when the comber therefore lashed the wool into the holding comb, the subsequent strain of working or drawing out would cause these crossed fibres to coil round the teeth of the holding comb and so ensure a firmer holding of the mass—and, indeed, it was necessary that it should be so held or the action of the working comb would draw it entirely out of the teeth—but the consequence was that when the operative came to draw out the end that had been worked, the other end became so firmly fixed that it could only be extracted by breaking a considerable portion of the long fibres; by this means the noil or refuse was greatly increased, and the most valuable part of the wool (*i.e.* the top) in the same proportion diminished.' As a remedy Heilmann adopted the principle known as the Nip. 'By means of two nipping instruments which closed upon the fleece as it was being fed into the machine, the point end was held in position till it was combed out by a revolving drum furnished with comb teeth; the cleaned end was then carried forward and taken hold of by another pair of nippers, till the other end had been treated in a similar manner. The same process was repeated again and again. By this gentle treatment the loss sustained under the old system was avoided.'

While the Alsatian inventor was working out his ideas two English inventors, Donisthorpe and Lister, were striving towards the same goal and they reached independently somewhat similar results. 'Before Mr. Heilmann's patent was heard of,' Lister has affirmed, 'we had succeeded in mastering all the difficulties connected with the invention.' Donisthorpe was the first to conceive the project, and his machine was the starting-point of Lister's subsequent improvements. Afterwards the two men collaborated and the Nip machine (1851) was the product of their combined investigations. The three difficulties which they had to overcome were 'to comb perfectly, to prevent clogging in the process, and to reduce the proportion of noil or waste in the course of the operation. When they took the matter in hand there was no machine existing that answered all these requirements, but ultimately they arrived at the Nip machine in which the tuft of wool was drawn by a nipper [a pair of curved metal jaws] through a gill comb. They drew the wool through the teeth [of the great circle] horizontally, while Heilmann drew the teeth through the wool in a circle *i.e.* worked the ends of the wool by a circular carder.'

Isaac Holden, another prominent figure in the worsted industry, was born in Scotland. Ambitious to solve a problem which was taxing the ingenuity of his contemporaries to the utmost, he turned his attention to wool-combing and in collaboration with Lister designed the combing machine known as the Square Motion. Its principles can best be described in Holden's own words. The fault of earlier working combs (the screw gill working combs) 'was that the comb was pushed away too slowly by the screw after it entered the beard[1] close to the circular comb-head. The consequence was that the comb was locked in the beard if it entered it near the comb-head; and therefore to avoid this it was necessary to strike into it at some distance, and even then to use coarse and strong combs. The result was bad combing. This evil, I felt certain, could be avoided by the mode of working I conceived of—the Square Motion—viz. striking a fine comb into the beard near to the comb-head and at once pushing it away from it to avoid locking. The whole secret of the invention lay in this discovery, the necessity of pushing away quickly, so simple at first sight but difficult to conceive and appreciate at that early period; and though so apparently simple it was the result of much continued thought.' Holden's account serves to elucidate the two cardinal principles of the Square Motion machine. Firstly, the teeth of the working comb are made to enter the fibres of wool at the exact point where the ends of the fibres are held in position by the circular comb, in order to leave as little uncombed wool or noil as possible. Secondly, no sooner are the teeth of the working comb inserted in the teeth of the circular comb than they are instantaneously withdrawn, in order to prevent the locking of the combs and consequent breakage of the fibres. It is claimed for the Square Motion machine that 'it is a perfect imitation of the mode of working of the hand-comber, and the work it accomplishes resembles that of the hand-comber. It produces the same polish, the same curl or crochet, the same softness and loftiness, and the same high spinning qualities, the length of fibre in top and noil being well preserved.'

One last invention needs to be mentioned. In 1853 James Noble, a working mechanic, took out a patent for the machine which bears his name. It was designed on novel principles and discarded the features of the Nip machine, in which the combing

[1] The fringe of the fibres of wool.

was 'largely done by mechanism external to the circle.' Noble
conceived the idea of two circles—a circular revolving comb
carrying the wool and a circular working comb inside the
revolving comb. His machine was 'a compact circular structure
in which the main circle stands at a height of about two feet
from the ground. Inside this circle are two smaller ones, about
a foot and a half in diameter, each touching the main circle at
opposite points on the interior of its circumference. All rotate
in one direction. The slivers of wool to be combed are rolled up
in creels attached to the outer side of the great circle and travel-
ling with it. They move up automatically in turn, and fall on
to the pins of the circles at the points where the outer one
touches the two inner ones. A brush, rising and falling rapidly,
dabs the wool down among the two sets of pins and there true
combing begins.'

APPENDIX TO CHAPTER SEVEN

AN OFFICIAL REPORT[1] on the wool textile industry (1947) has pointed out that 'most of the main machines are extremely durable. With proper maintenance, and in the absence of fundamental improvements, they can be made to produce with comparative efficiency for periods of well over fifty years. Some of the woollen carding machinery in use is over eighty years old; nearly a quarter of the worsted spindles and a higher proportion of the woollen spindles date from last century; and many of the looms have been in use for fifty years or more. This great durability has meant that normal replacements have been low, and that there has been no overwhelming pressure to install new equipment at frequent intervals. The low rate of replacement has tended to weaken the incentive to develop or experiment with new machinery. In most branches of the industry there have been few really fundamental improvements for at least a generation. The small detailed improvements in design have been incorporated in old machines by re-building at the mill or by the use of accessories fitted by textile machinery makers or firms of jobbing engineers. The machinery has come to have some of the characteristics of house property: an existing machine after thorough reconditioning may prove as satisfactory or almost as satisfactory as a new one of the same type.'

The mechanical equipment of the wool textile industry, as it existed in 1947, is summarized in the report as follows:

'(a) *Wool Scouring and Carbonizing*

Fifty years ago carbonizing machinery was relatively primitive with oven treatment and outside drying. To-day there is a complicated range of machinery using automatic and continuous processes.

(b) *Worsted Carding and Combing*

There have been few significant improvements in worsted carding and combing machinery for many years. Machines installed before 1914, if well maintained and modernized, can

[1] Board of Trade, *Working Party Report: Wool* (1947).

and do give as good a performance as new ones. Very few of
the combs, but a much higher proportion of the cards, date back
to 1900 or earlier. A correspondingly high proportion of the
combs are of recent construction.

(c) *Woollen Carding*

We have had no information on the average age of woollen
carding engines in the industry, but examples have been quoted
to us of jobbing orders for machinery built in 1865, 1868 and
1872; and in view of the comparatively rapid progress in the
design of this machinery, it is difficult to regard these as other
than obsolete. From this and other indications we are disposed
to think that there is more room for improvement in the
equipment on the woollen than on the worsted side of the
industry.

(d) *Worsted Spinning*

In worsted spinning 60 per cent. of the spindles are cap,
19 per cent. flyer, 7 per cent. ring, and 14 per cent. mule.
Apart from the self-doffer, there have been few recent changes
in worsted spinning; 24 per cent. of the machinery dates back
to 1900 or earlier.

(e) *Woollen Spinning*

In woollen spinning mule spindles form 97 per cent. of the
total. There has been a slight increase in continuous spinning
but frames are still insignificant in relation to mules. The
proportion of spindles installed before 1900 is not known but
is almost certainly higher than in worsted spinning. Changes
in the standard models immediately before the war were
designed to give higher speeds, increased holding capacity of
packages and easier manipulation. The spinning speed of mule
spindles in woollen spinning has been increased by 50–60 per
cent. by the use of spindles in separate units, without vibration
and with an increase in productivity of about 35 per cent.

(f) *Weaving*

Towards the end of the last century there was a displacement
of narrow by broad looms, which allowed an increased weight
of cloth to be woven on a given number of looms. Although no

comparable figures are available, this trend has presumably continued since. A second change has been the increase in the speed of the looms. In 1878 in the woollen section of the industry the standard loom ran at 50 picks per minute. By 1904 the 100 pick loom was coming into use, and 1926 was the normal type in the Yorkshire tweed trade. The Balfour Committee in 1927, in commenting on this change, noted that there had also been an increase in speed in the fine worsted section, but stated that in ordinary worsted weaving the maximum speed of operation had been reached twenty or thirty years previously. The maximum speed of textile machinery obtainable without damage to quality is a matter of debate; the limits vary with the physical properties of the fibre. Nor is it only in weaving that there is difficulty in finding the optimum speed consistent with quality. In wool-combing, for example, too high a speed would cause damage to the fibre and inefficient processing, and would have a bad effect on the quality of the work done. In spinning the highest qualities of yarn are generally spun on mules, which have a lower output per spindle-hour. In weaving, if the machinery is run too fast, breakages occur and the cost of mending goes up; if yarn of greater tensile strength is used, the quality of the cloth is affected. While there has been a gradual and progressive adjustment of the yarn to enable it to run at high speeds—it remains true that, if too much twist is put on the yarn to make it strong enough to stand very high speeds, the cloth becomes unsaleable. It is doubtful whether the standard loom of to-day shows more than a trifling improvement in speed in comparison with looms built forty years ago. But the modern loom, running at 110 picks per minute, gives as high a quality of cloth and can be operated much more readily on the two looms to a weaver system than the older looms.

The most important change in the design of the loom between the wars was the introduction of the automatic loom. This is in general use in the United States, where it is made by the only two firms of loom manufacturers in that country. Of the 40,000 looms installed, 28,800 are automatic. In Great Britain only a limited number of automatic looms have so far been installed.

(g) *Dyeing*

Many improvements have been made in dyeing and finishing machinery during the last twenty years. Considerable use has been made of stainless steel.

(h) *General Considerations*

If it were our aim to transform the industry into one making goods of medium quality by mass-production methods, it would be desirable to make a drastic change in the whole layout in favour of automatic machinery and working two or even three shifts per day. If however quality is the first objective, and few firms are free to specialize exclusively in a narrow range of products because of the market risks involved, then the type of equipment required would be much closer to that now in use. It is our view that nothing should be done to destroy or damage the reputation of the industry for high quality cloth. But we believe that there is room for a large extension in the use of automatic machinery, particularly in winding, warping and weaving.'

CHAPTER EIGHT

The Nineteenth and Twentieth Centuries

IT IS OFTEN ASSUMED that the introduction of machinery forthwith created the factory system and extinguished the domestic system. This view needs to be considerably qualified. The factory owners—for instance, Benjamin Gott—undoubtedly made their appearance very early in the nineteenth century. They were recruited partly from the ranks of successful clothiers who bought machinery and started mills, but mainly from the class of merchants who were already responsible for the finishing processes and now turned manufacturers by taking over from the clothiers all the earlier processes. None the less the domestic system held its ground among the working clothiers of the West Riding of Yorkshire even beyond the middle of the nineteenth century; and as late as 1856 only about one-half of those engaged in the woollen industry in Yorkshire were employed in factories. The reasons for the survival of the domestic system in Yorkshire were as follows. In the first place, the adoption of the power-loom in the woollen industry was very gradual. In 1835 Yorkshire contained but 688 power-looms for woollen weaving or less than one-fourth of the number used in worsted weaving. The slow penetration of the power-loom can be explained on technical grounds. The essential characteristic of woollen cloth is its felting property which enables the fibres to be interlaced; hence woollen yarn must be spun more loosely. This made weaving a difficult operation since the threads were easily broken; and so the power-loom worked no faster than the hand-loom (the shuttle flying about forty times a minute), whereas the worsted power-loom made a hundred and sixty picks a minute. In the second place, the small clothiers displayed a remarkable adaptability to circumstances. Instead of resisting the new conditions of production, they turned them to their own account. The fly shuttle had been adopted earlier in Yorkshire than elsewhere; and, recognizing the advantages of machinery, the domestic manufacturers now combined their resources in order to obtain machines for their own use. The numerous woollen mills scattered throughout the West Riding were said to be chiefly owned by groups of clothiers. Here is a description of joint-stock woollen mills written by an inspector of factories in 1843: 'The history of joint-stock company woollen mills exhibits a singular instance of energy amongst the smaller capitalists of the manufacturing districts. In the formation of a company mill a number of clothiers (for they must be clothiers to be partners) of small capital meet together and determine to become a company of so many partners, from ten to fifty, in shares generally of £25 each—each person taking as many shares as his capital will enable him. With this subscribed capital deeds of partnership are drawn, land is bought, a mill erected and machinery put up. The processes which are carried on in these company mills are scribbling, carding, slubbing, and fulling cloth, which are the preparatory processes of the cloth manufacture; and the remaining processes—viz. spinning, warping, weaving and burling—are done at home by members of the family or by persons employed for that purpose.' The wool was sent to the mill to be scribbled and slubbed, then returned to the clothier in whose home it was spun and woven (on a hand-loom), again sent to the mill to be fulled, and afterwards sold in an unfinished state to the merchant who dyed and finished it ready for use.

Outside the ranks of the West Riding clothiers the introduction of machinery aroused violent opposition. 'Who does not consider the employment of machinery,' asked a writer, 'one of the greatest evils that ever befell the country? And who would not rejoice at a return to the rude habits of industry which once characterized the country, and under whose sway Englishmen were healthy, happy and contented?' It would be erroneous to regard this hostility as wholly unreasonable—although the benefits of machinery were undoubtedly considerable. Firstly it effected a great economy of labour, cheapened the price of commodities, stimulated the demand, and so ultimately led to increased production and expansion of trade.

L

Secondly it enabled work which was often unpleasant and unhealthy to be done by motive-power instead of by hand. 'I think the most beneficial consequences have resulted from the introduction of machinery, particularly to the scribblers. The scribblers need to work in bodies and very close together, and on wool that from the oil and smell became quite obnoxious. They were a poor, sickly, decrepit race of beings.' Hand-loom weaving itself was not necessarily an unhealthy occupation, though weavers prior to the adoption of the fly shuttle were liable to breast disorders, but it was tedious and laborious. Thirdly most of the work done in the textile industries was already mechanical in character even before the use of mechanical devices. The processes of carding, combing, spinning, weaving and dressing, consisted in the monotonous repetition of certain movements of the hand, and afforded little or no scope for an expression of individuality which is the justification of true craftsmanship. And finally the creation of factories, if it subjected the worker to a novel and strict discipline, had its compensation in the shorter and more regular hours ultimately imposed by the state; and it was preferable that the preparatory processes, at any rate, should be carried on in large airy buildings (as they were later) rather than in crowded tenements where the same room had often to serve as a workshop and living place.

Nevertheless there was a reverse side to the picture. The invention of machinery meant a great displacement of labour. The apologists for machinery contended at the time—and the argument has been repeated ever since—that machinery creates in the long run a demand for more labour than is at the moment displaced. The expansion of industry, resulting from the cheapening of production, causes many more hands to be employed than when commodities are hand-made and relatively dear. Thus Dyer, speaking of Paul's invention, bade the spinners not to lose heart:

> Nor hence, ye nymphs, let anger cloud your brows;
> The more is wrought, the more is still requir'd.

In this connexion it is fair to remember two things. The belief

was widespread among the woollen operatives that the sources
of our wool supply were strictly limited, and so there was no
possibility of a great extension of the woollen manufacture
accompanied by an increase in the amount of employment.
The potentialities of Australia as a wool-producing country
were practically unknown at the end of the eighteenth century,
although a few had a vision of the future. Moreover a man
whose skill, his sole property, was rendered useless by a new
machine would find it poor consolation to be told that at some
distant date there would be room for additional labour in his
industry.

We have now to describe the progress of mechanical inventions in the woollen and worsted industries.

1. *The Fly Shuttle.* The earliest of the modern textile inventions, the fly shuttle, was used by the West Riding in Kay's own
lifetime; yet in the west country its adoption was belated.
Dyer, whose poem was published in 1757, assumed that two
weavers were still needed to work the broad loom.

> If the broader mantle be the task
> He chooses some companion to his toil.

Adam Smith in *The Wealth of Nations*, published in 1776, noted
'three very capital improvements' in the woollen industry—
namely, the substitution of the spinning-wheel for the distaff
and spindle, the use of fulling mills, and machines for facilitating
the winding of yarn and the proper arrangement of the warp
and weft before they were fixed on the loom—but he omits any
mention of Kay's device. The fly shuttle began to be adopted
in the west country about the beginning of the nineteenth century; yet as late as 1822 a request was made that soldiers should
be quartered at Frome, 'in order to prevent any disturbances
during the introduction of spring looms which will now be
generally used here as they have long been in Yorkshire,
Gloucestershire and Wiltshire.'

2. *Spinning Machinery.* While the west country weavers were
slowly reconciling themselves to improvements in the mode of
weaving invented as far back as 1733, the preliminary processes

were being revolutionized in the north. In the last decade of the eighteenth century machinery was used in scribbling—a kind of preparatory carding intended to separate the fibres of the wool; in carding itself; and in slubbing—a process between carding and spinning by which the wool slivers were joined together, drawn out into a continuous thread and slightly twisted. The first machine in Yorkshire for spinning worsted yarn (the water-frame) was erected at Addingham as early as 1787.[1] A few years later (1794) it was introduced into Bradford, where it was accompanied by an attempt to erect a factory in the town. The residents of the future metropolis of the worsted industry raised strenuous opposition on the plea that the steam-engine was a 'smoky nuisance,' and threatened the manufacturer with legal proceedings. 'Take notice,' they warned him, 'that if you shall presume to erect any steam-engine for the manufacture of cotton or wool we shall, if the same be found a nuisance, seek such redress as the law shall give.' The effort to arrest the march of industrial progress was abortive, for hand-spinning steadily lost ground; the opening of the nineteenth century was marked by the erection of a worsted mill at Bradford to house the water-frame, and in the second decade the spinning-wheel began to be generally superseded in the worsted manufacture. The ease with which machine-spinning achieved its victory over hand-spinning may be attributed to three factors. The spinners were women and children who could offer no effective resistance to the introduction of machinery; the demand for female and child labour in the factories created fresh avenues of employment for them; the weavers profited by the increased production of yarn and did not oppose the new methods. While worsted spinning was revolutionized in the north, it continued on the traditional lines in Norfolk which had no yarn factory until 1834.

The factory system achieved a speedier victory in the Yorkshire worsted industry than in the woollen industry, where spinning was still carried on as a household occupation. The

---

[1] The first worsted factory with water-frames had been erected in 1784 at Dolphin Holme in Lancashire. At first machinery was worked by horse or water-power; the use of steam followed shortly after. (A steam cotton mill was erected at Papplewick in Nottinghamshire in 1785.)

reason for the contrast may be sought for in differences of economic organization. The worsted manufacture in the north appears, from its inception, to have been more definitely capitalist in character than the woollen, possibly because its introduction was due to the enterprise of capitalist pioneers. Its leaders, at any rate, had a larger command of capital than the domestic clothiers and they specialized to a greater extent. A trade which is highly specialized and equipped with considerable capital has a stronger inducement to adopt the most efficient methods of production.

3. *The Power-Loom.* The conquest of hand-loom weaving by the power-loom was a much slower process than the conquest of hand-spinning by the frame or mule. Besides the hostility of weavers which made the introduction of steam-looms a venturesome undertaking, there were technical reasons for the tardy progress. In the case of the woollen industry the loosely spun yarn was not suited to the operations of the power-loom so well as the worsted yarn which was spun hard and tight. Yet even in the worsted industry—where steam-weaving established its predominance earlier than in the other branch— the adoption of the power-loom was delayed on account of the necessity for frequent stoppages of the machine in order to size[1] or dress the warp as it unrolled from the yarn beam. This obstacle was only removed in 1803 when William Radcliffe took out a patent for a dressing machine which starched the warp before it was bound upon the loom. Nor was the saving of labour at first impressive; as late as 1819 it was said that 'one person cannot attend upon more than two power-looms, and it is still problematical whether this saving of labour counterbalances the expense of power and machinery.' Again the hand-loom weavers submitted to the fatal policy of 'lowering the dyke;' they carried on an unequal contest with machinery, in which they maintained a precarious existence by submitting to repeated reductions of wages. The sacrifice they thus made retarded, although it could not avert, the ultimate extinction of their occupation.

[1] Sizing means to saturate the warp with paste to strengthen it, and so enable it to bear the operation of weaving.

The first attempt to introduce the power-loom naturally provoked violent antagonism. There was a serious outbreak in Bradford in 1826 when popular resentment flared up in a determined but unsuccessful effort to wreck the machines. It was followed by a general adoption of power-looms on the part of the worsted manufacturers in Yorkshire though not in the west country, as will be seen from the following table:[1]

TABLE SHOWING THE NUMBER OF POWER-LOOMS USED IN WOOLLEN AND WORSTED FACTORIES IN 1835.[2]

County	Woollen	Worsted
Yorkshire	688[3]	2,856[3]
Lancashire	1,142	—
Westmorland	8	—
Cheshire	8	—
Leicestershire	89[4]	—
Gloucestershire	4	—
Somersetshire	74	—
Montgomeryshire	4	—
Northumberland	6	—

4. *The Gig Mill and Shearing Frame.* The gig mill for raising the nap on the cloth contained a cylinder covered with teasles. The economy in labour was said to be considerable, a machine managed by one man and two boys doing the work of eighteen men and six boys. The shearing frame, which cut the nap, had several pairs of shears worked by power. It also effected a great saving of labour. Moreover it was alleged to be impossible to cut the cloth from end to end evenly with hand-shears, whereas a machine administered regular strokes with 'mathematical nicety.'

[1] It will be observed that Norfolk is not represented by any power-looms.
[2] In 1856 the number of power-looms in the United Kingdom was 14,453 in the woollen industry and 38,956 in the worsted industry.
[3] There were also 226 power-looms used for woollen and worsted, and 307 for worsted and cotton.
[4] Used for woollen and worsted.

The introduction of machinery into the finishing of cloth aroused dissension as early as the fifteenth century. A statute of 1495 forbade shearmen to use 'instruments of iron' in place of 'the broad shears;' and a statute of 1551 prohibited the gig mill. The latter injunction does not appear to have taken effect. A writer in 1803 remarked that the gig mill had been employed in Gloucestershire and Wiltshire on coarse white cloth 'longer than anyone can remember,' although no strict proof could be adduced to identify this machine with that mentioned in the statute of 1551. However the attempt to apply the gig mill to fine white cloth and medley cloth excited strenuous resistance among the workmen in Wiltshire; and the manufacturers there were forced to send their cloth to be 'gigged' in Gloucestershire which contained public mills working for the clothiers on commission. Their example was imitated by the manufacturers of Somersetshire, who refrained from using the gig mill at home to avoid riots. In the West Riding, where most kinds of machinery were introduced with greater ease than elsewhere, the bitter opposition was even more protracted than in the west country: at the end of the eighteenth century the gig mill, while not unknown, was still exceptional and mainly cloths were finished by hand owing to the hostility of the men. A Yorkshire manufacturer Hirst (who wrote an account of his career as a clothier) declared that as late as 1810 'if a Yorkshire manufacturer went into a market with one from the west of England and they had both a piece of cloth manufactured from the same wool, the latter would get a better price by nearly one-half'—the west country having machinery for finishing cloth which Yorkshire employers dared not introduce; and 'it was impossible to produce so good a finishing by manual labour.' The fury of the Luddite rioters in 1812 was directed primarily against the gig mill and shearing frame. The Luddites 'were regularly organized and trained. After demolishing the works of Mr. Foster of Horbury in Yorkshire their leader ordered them into a field, and their numbers (each man having a number to conceal his name) being called over he dismissed them by the word of command: "The work is done, disperse!" The time occupied in the business of mustering, destruction and dispersing did not exceed twenty minutes.' A verse of the croppers' ballad ran:

> Great Enoch[1] still shall lead the van,
> Stop him who dare! Stop him who can!
> Press forward every gallant man
> With hatchet, pike and gun!
> O! the cropper lads for me,
> The gallant lads for me,
> Who with lusty stroke
> The shear frames broke,
> The cropper lads for me.

The Yorkshire cloth-finishers were better organized than other classes of textile workers in the West Riding, and they maintained close relations with shearmen's clubs in the rest of the country. This no doubt explains the stiff fight they were able to put up against the introduction of machinery into their branch of industry. Nevertheless the ultimate issue of the struggle was the complete downfall of the shearmen, who failed to prevent the displacement of manual processes by mechanical contrivances. Between 1806 and 1817 the number of gig mills in Yorkshire was said to have increased from 5 to 72; the number of shears worked by machinery from 100 to 1,462; and out of 3,378 shearmen no less than 1,170 were out of work while 1,445 were only partially employed.

5. *Wool-Combing*. The invention of the combing machine excited a storm of opposition. It was assailed especially on the ground that it 'diminished labour to an alarming degree.' Parliament was inundated with petitions from all parts of the realm, the burden of the complaint being that fifty thousand workmen with their wives and families would be reduced to beggary. 'One machine only, with the assistance of one person and four or five children, will perform as much labour as thirty men in the customary manual manner.' The arguments advanced in support of machinery in cotton, silk and linen, claimed the wool-combers, did not apply to wool textiles.

---

[1] 'Enoch' was the name given to the big hammer employed in the work of destruction.

'Almost any quantity of the raw materials can be procured to supply the manufacturers [of cotton, silk and linen], which by enlarging their trade still retains an equal or greater number of persons in employ; whereas but a specific quantity [of wool] can be obtained.' It was believed that 'the growth of wool is definite and never equals the ability of the wool-combers to manufacture.' Hence it was 'not possible to increase the raw material [wool] beyond the present quantity,' and so increase the amount of employment by extending production.

Reviewing the tardy progress of machinery as a whole, it is not surprising that a wool stapler (Luccock) writing in 1805 contrasted the stagnation of the wool textile industry with the vigour displayed by its younger rival—'In the woollen manufacture only small capitals are employed; no extensive works are constructed for carrying them on; the machines are simple and old; the workmen are jealous of innovation, always obstinate. [Whereas the cotton manufacture exhibited] large capitals, immense establishments, a highly speculative spirit, great confidence, and a combination of all the productions of modern genius.'

All periods of transition are apt to be periods of distress. As the old order yields place to the new, the instability of the social organism throws to the surface all that is worst in its constitution. A harsh destiny soon overtakes those who are unable to adapt themselves with ease and rapidity to the changed condition of things—for the race is to the swift and the strong, and the weak and the feeble 'go to the wall.' In the case of the 'Industrial Revolution' the evils of the transition from implements to machinery were aggravated by a protracted war which diverted the energies of the country from the normal channels of industrial activity, while the free development of the national resources was shackled by the unparalleled growth of the national debt coupled with a fantastical fiscal system. We relate in the following paragraphs the sufferings of the hand-loom weavers, the story of whose extinction constitutes the most melancholy chapter in the history of the textile industries and a classic example of the triumph of economic progress at the expense of social welfare.

The immediate effects of the 'Industrial Revolution' upon the hand-loom weavers were beneficial. They profited by the enormous output of yarn from the spinning factories, and owing to the increased demand for their labour they reaped a harvest of high wages. The muslin weavers of Bolton may be cited in illustration of their flourishing condition, though the prosperity of other weavers was much more subdued. 'The trade was that of a gentleman,' said a witness before a parliamentary committee in 1834. 'They brought home their work in top boots and ruffled shirts, carried a cane and in some instances took a coach.' Many weavers at that time, we are told, 'used to walk about the streets with a five-pound Bank of England note spread out under their hat-bands; they would smoke none but long churchwarden pipes, and objected to the intrusion of any other handicraftsmen into the particular rooms in the public houses which they frequented. This prosperity did not continue, and few operatives endured greater privations than the hand-loom weavers of Bolton for the succeeding fifty years.'

The gradual deterioration which took place in the position of the hand-loom weavers was due primarily to the drastic fall in wages. Its sweeping nature may be gauged from a comparison of the average wages paid by a Bolton manufacturer over a term of thirty-five years for weaving a piece of cloth, twenty-four yards, the measure of a week's work:

					£	s.	d.
Between	1797 and	1803	the price paid was		1	6	8
,,	1804 ,,	1810	,,	,,	1	0	0
,,	1811 ,,	1817	,,	,,	0	14	7
,,	1818 ,,	1824	,,	,,	0	8	9
,,	1825 ,,	1831	,,	,,	0	6	4
,,	1832 ,,	1833	,,	,,	0	5	6

In the first period a weaver could purchase with his wages 25 lb. of flour, $35\frac{1}{2}$ lb. of oatmeal, $206\frac{1}{2}$ lb. of potatoes, and 14 lb. of meat—in all 281 lb. of provisions. In the fifth period he could only purchase 10 lb. of flour, $14\frac{1}{2}$ lb. of oatmeal, 55 lb. of potatoes, and $3\frac{1}{2}$ lb. of meat—in all 83 lb. of provisions. Thus his wages in money declined nearly 80 per cent. and the reduction involved a proportionate decline in his command over the necessaries of life. According to the hand-loom commissioners, whose report was published in 1840, the wages of worsted weavers in the West Riding working full time seldom exceeded six or seven shillings a week; but, as they rarely had full employment, their actual earnings fell below this amount. In the west of England wages were sometimes still more exiguous than in the north. The weavers' union estimated in 1828 that the minimum sum sufficient to keep a man, his wife and three children was 15s. 8d. a week; and since weavers earned much less, the commissioners reported that the condition of a pauper in the workhouse was superior to that of a weaver's family. A *Poem by an Operative of Keighley* (1834) recites:

The weavers, a set of poor souls,
With clothes on their backs much like riddles for holes;
With faces quite pale and eyes sunk in the head,
As if the whole race were half-famished for bread.

Indeed, when these wretches you happen to meet,
You think they are shadows you see in the street;
For their thin water-porridge is all they can get,
And even with that they are often hard set.

There were several reasons for the fall in wages. One was that weavers competed with machinery. The power-loom was introduced only gradually but it set the pace; and the ability of the power-loom master to undersell the hand-loom master forced the latter to cut rates of payment. The ever-present menace that machinery might be introduced sapped the weavers' spirit of resistance. Again the weavers were fatally handicapped by the weakness of their bargaining force because they were not organized in strong trade unions. Their failure to combine was due partly to their isolation and dispersion over the country-side; partly to extreme poverty which could not stand the strain of a weekly contribution to the trade union funds; and partly to the fact that the instrument upon which they worked was their own property, and if it stood idle they alone suffered. Another important factor was that the trade was easily acquired; and, as it was remarked, this facility made hand-loom weaving 'a receptacle for the destitute from all other classes.' As the result of the inventions in spinning the existing body of weavers was unable to cope with the abundance of yarn, and the high prices at first paid for weaving attracted hands from every other occupation. In particular agricultural labourers flocked to the large industrial centres, and a lower grade of hand-loom weavers was created. This invasion of the urban labour market had pernicious consequences; it not only swelled the numbers of the weavers to excess but exposed them to unfair competition, for the newcomers accustomed to a low standard of living were prepared to accept low rates of remuneration. Nor were farm workers the sole competitors of the town weavers. The worsted weavers of Yorkshire attributed their distressed state, among other factors, to the immigration of Irish workmen who were compelled by their poverty to crowd the English labour market. The efforts of the weavers to improve their situation were fatal in the extreme. In order to eke out their scanty resources they put their children at an early age to weaving, thus involving them in the meshes of the same remorseless destiny in which they were themselves inextricably entangled.

The fate which overtook the hand-loom weavers eventually befell the wool-combers, though the latter did not succumb without resistance. Their most famous strike broke out in 1825 at Bradford. It lasted five months and affected twenty thousand men. The strikers enjoyed considerable sympathy in their struggle to raise wages, and received contributions from all parts of the kingdom. To smash their union, the masters declared a lock-out and closed down the mills. They also induced the mill owners at Halifax, Keighley and other centres to pledge themselves to discharge all combers and weavers in their employment who supported the Bradford union with funds. The strike was remarkable for 'the peaceable and orderly manner' in which it was carried on, and it is said that 'not a single outrage or breach of peace' occurred during its course. Nevertheless the men failed to overcome the tenacity of the masters, and the only result of the ruinous contest was to stimulate the introduction of machinery.

The strike of 1825 marks the turning-point in the history of the hand-combers, whose condition now underwent rapid deterioration. Their sufferings were intense, they worked long hours in an over-heated atmosphere, and their toil was wretchedly remunerated. Their spasmodic attempts to alleviate their distress were ineffectual. They no longer held the whip-hand over the employers, who were able to utilize machinery which every day was increasing in efficiency; and the recognition of their weakness constrained the hand-combers to adopt a humbler tone, which was in striking contrast to their proud and defiant attitude in the eighteenth century. In 1840 the Bradford Wool-Combers' Association drew up a statement which ran: 'Knowing the evil effects of turn-outs [strikes] we desire if possible to avoid them in future. We know that they can only be avoided by our masters uniting with us for the good of each, and all angry feelings or animosities which exist in the bosoms of the employers or employed being banished and each other's interests considered reciprocal. It must have been evident to every master who has reduced the wages of his workmen that, previous to the reduction, it was scarcely possible for any of his wool-combers to obtain an honest living by their own hand-labour. But now that the reduction has taken place our sufferings are augmented and our lives have become miserable. We are compelled to work from fourteen to sixteen hours per day, and with all this sweat and toil we are not able to procure sufficient of the necessaries of life wherewith to subsist on.' The hand-combers had clung to the conviction that Cartwright's machine would never prove workable, but the improvements described in the previous chapter gave the death-blow to their fond anticipations. The middle of the nineteenth century may be taken as the period at which hand-combing as an industrial process became to all intents and purposes an extinct industry.

During the 'Industrial Revolution' the great mass of textile workers saw in state intervention their only hope of salvation, and they appealed to the statute-book which still enshrined in its pages the economic usages of an earlier age. It would be wrong to condemn their attitude as one of impracticable conservatism: the responsibility must rest, rather, with those who discarded the traditional safeguards bequeathed from the past for the protection of the working class but failed to devise fresh ones.

Although the compulsory assessment of wages had been abolished (in so far as the woollen industry was concerned) in 1757, the apprenticeship clauses of the Statute of Apprentices— while actually obsolete—were still technically in force. The weavers now had recourse to the old legislation in order to protect themselves from the competition of cheap labour; they raised a fund for the purpose, and employed attorneys to bring actions on their behalf against 'illegal' workmen who had not been properly trained. Attempts were made at the same time to enforce the Weavers' Act of 1555 which limited the number of looms—in the hope of checking the factory system and preserving the domestic system. The clothiers thereupon appealed to Parliament for protection and demanded the repeal of all restrictions. In spite of numerous petitions the suspension bill became law in 1803, and year by year a suspending act was passed until 1809 when the whole code of restrictive legislation relating to the assize and 'true making' of cloth, compulsory apprenticeship, limitation of looms and the prohibition of gig mills—the heritage of Tudor statesmanship— was swept away in obedience to the demand of the woollen manufacturers for complete industrial freedom.

We must now view the state of English wool textiles during the present century.

The structure of the wool textile industry in England—as on the Continent and in the United States—is different in each of the two main branches. It is usually horizontal in the case of the worsted section, that is, combing, spinning, weaving, dyeing and finishing are operated by separate firms.[1] It is usually vertical in the case of the woollen section, that is, the whole series of processes is operated by a single firm. There are conspicuous exceptions to the general rule: some worsted establishments undertake more than one process, and some woollen

[1] Of 617 worsted establishments in 1935—264 did spinning, 195 weaving, 62 combing, and 96 combined spinning and weaving.

establishments are restricted to spinning. The contrast between
the two sections may be explained on several grounds. For one
thing the worsted manufacturer is enabled to specialize in the
production of a limited range of qualities instead of having to
provide for the varied needs of an integrated economy. For
another thing a considerable export trade in worsted tops and
yarns, coupled with a home trade in hosiery yarns and the
vagaries of worsted fashions, have encouraged the separation
of processes. However the main reason lies in the nature of the
machinery employed in worsted spinning and combing which
cannot be readily adapted to different materials, for instance,
crossbred in place of merino wool; whereas it is claimed that
'a woollen mill can spin anything with two ends to it.' Furthermore in woollen fabrics both yarns of varying qualities and
materials other than wool may be utilized; this makes it
desirable to keep all the processes under centralized control if
the requisite standard is to be attained. Finally technical
considerations indicate why dyeing and finishing are done on
commission in the worsted but not in the woollen branch. Owing
to the general concentration on a single process which prevails
in the worsted section, it is the practice for a firm to do work
for other firms on commission. Thus combing firms take wool
either from a manufacturer or a merchant (known as a top-
maker) and deliver back tops and noils; in addition they may
themselves make tops for sale. Even mills which are engaged
in spinning may have some kinds of yarn manufactured on a
commission basis.

We are accustomed to associate the capitalist system with
large-scale production: but in many industries the unit of production is relatively small. One of the outstanding features of
the wool textile industry in England is the size of the factories.
According to the census of production (1935) they numbered
about fifteen hundred and employed a quarter of a million
workers. Barely more than a hundred factories had 400 or more
workers (only nineteen exceeded 1,000 workers)—and they
accounted for one-third of the total employment; fourteen
hundred factories had over 10 and less than 400 workers; while
eight hundred factories (not in the census) did not rise above 10

workers. Nearly half the factories were of moderate size, that is, they ranged between 50 and 200 workers. It must also be observed that the establishments engaged in the worsted branch were larger than those in the woollen branch. Where there exists a multitude of small firms the usual consequence is to sharpen rivalry between them; prices tend to be governed more by the laws of supply and demand than when a few large firms can regulate prices by agreement among themselves. In practice, however, owing to specialization—the concentration on special lines—competition in the sale of similar products is restricted to a comparatively small group. We are told that 'the range of products is enormous; several hundred types of cloth are manufactured and even these require further subdivision according to style, pattern and finish.' The small size of the normal establishments is closely connected with the fact that they are mostly owned by individuals or by private limited companies, though public joint-stock companies are not unknown and tend to increase.

After the cloth is ready for the market, several channels of sale are at the command of the manufacturer. He may sell direct to those who make up men's and women's clothes on a large scale; more than half the trade is said to fall into this category. Next he may sell to merchants, who supply either retailers or small garment-makers. These merchants may buy the cloth dyed and finished; alternatively (like their predecessors in the eighteenth century) they may buy the cloth in the grey and have it dyed and finished by a commission firm. Merchants still continue to play an important role in the marketing of cloth—not only as intermediaries between the mill and the small consumers, but because they carry stocks and so materially assist the manufacturer by placing with him bulk orders for his specialized products. Again the manufacturer may sell to wholesalers, who handle other goods besides textiles and supply retailers. Lastly the manufacturer may sell to retailers, though this does not constitute an appreciable percentage of total sales. Thus direct trade between those who make cloth and those who fabricate it into garments exists only in the first category. In the other categories a middleman (merchant, wholesaler or retailer) serves as the channel between manufacturer and consumer.

A conspicuous feature of the textile industry over the past hundred years is the remarkable steadiness in the volume of employment. The number of workers was approximately a quarter of a million in the middle of the nineteenth century, and it fluctuated around about that figure down to the second world war when it suffered a sharp contraction.[1] The normal variations due to changes in demand for textile goods have been of the magnitude of 10 per cent. or less—for example, the number of workers mounted to 275,000 in 1891; it fell to 235,000 a decade later; it had recovered to a quarter of a million another decade later; it rose to 260,000 in 1924; it had sunk to 227,000 in 1939. While the number of operatives remained comparatively stationary, the consumption of wool was more than trebled; this was rendered possible by the adoption of mechanical methods in place of manual processes and by the increasing efficiency of machinery. Women have always played a very large part in the textile industry even when it was organized on a domestic basis. In the census of 1851 they constituted two-fifths of the total; twenty years later, with the growth of the factory system, they had achieved a majority over men; and they have since consistently retained their preponderance. The ratio of women to men is normally 130:100 or over three times the national average for all occupations (which is roughly one woman for every three men). The disparity is explained by the number of women who remain in the industry after marriage or return to it in widowhood: in 1939 they amounted to about one-third of the female employees. Juveniles of both sexes under the age of eighteen averaged in recent years one-seventh of the total labour force: the proportion was higher in one branch of industry, namely, worsted spinning (where it was nearly one-fourth).

The distribution of the general body of workers depends upon the branch of industry in which they are engaged; the worsted section employs a greater number of hands than the woollen section, and worsted spinning absorbs more than any

---

[1] 1939—227,000; 1945—127,000. In 1951 it had recovered to 202,000.

M

other single process; the majority of the woollen operatives work for integrated firms carrying on the whole series of processes. The distribution of the sexes is determined by the nature of the occupation. Men preponderate in the preliminary processes of wool-sorting and wool-combing as well as in the final process of cloth-finishing; women preponderate in the manufacturing processes of spinning and weaving—in worsted spinning and weaving they are more than twice as numerous as males. Thus men are prominent at both ends of the industry and women in the intermediate stages.

In the opening decade of the present century, before two world wars produced catastrophic changes in the value of money, the earnings of operatives in wool textiles averaged about two shillings or half-a-crown a day for women and double for men.[1] Real wages as interpreted in terms of purchasing power may be gauged from the prices of common necessaries— bread was 5d. (per 4 lb. loaf); tea 20d. sugar 2d. cheese 7d. butter 12d. mutton and beef 9½d. potatoes ½d. (all these per lb.); eggs 13d. (per dozen), milk 3d. (per quart), coal 11d. (per cwt.). Rent and rates for a five-room house with kitchen, living room and bedrooms were 5s. to 9s. weekly; for a two-room house 2s. to 3s. An American investigator of housing conditions, the depressing legacy of the nineteenth century, observed that 'throughout Yorkshire the typical workmen's dwellings are built in straight rows of two-storey brick or stone buildings; there are no detached buildings, so we see these long rows of uniform dwellings.' The hours of labour were 55½ a week; after the first world war they were reduced to 48. Day and night shifts are operated mainly in the combing and spinning sections of the industry.

Attention has been drawn to the fact that the volume of employment in wool textiles moved within narrow limits of about 10 per cent. down to the second world war—in marked contrast with cotton textiles where in the preceding quarter of a century (1914–39) the volume of employment fell over 40 per

[1] Men received approximately 29s. as wool-sorters, 17s. as combers, 24s. as mule spinners, and 25s. as weavers; women were paid 9s. as frame spinners, 12s. as carders or combers, and 15s. as weavers. These are time wages (except weavers). Piece wages were 31s. (sorters) and 32s. (mule). Weavers were paid piece wages.

cent. Nevertheless the workers, while they remain within the industry, suffer from unemployment. The cycle of trade involves an alternation of booms and slumps; changes in home consumption, due to the demand for lighter and shorter clothes and for other new styles set by the weathercock of fashion, may bring prosperity to one district and depression to another; the erection of tariff barriers[1]—the McKinley tariff in the United States in 1895 led to the prediction that grass would grow in the streets of Bradford—hampers international trade; the competition of other fibres natural and artificial may divert the channels of consumption. Statistics of unemployment only became available when textile workers were brought under the national insurance scheme after the first world war. They show wide variations in employment during the twenties and thirties. The percentages of unemployment were approximately 7 in 1924, 21 in 1925, 10 in 1927, 36 in 1931, 10 in 1936, 6 in 1939; these figures give a better notion of the fluctuations than the average of a decade (in the thirties it was 20). It must not, however, be inferred that an unemployed person was out of work the whole year round; he might only have been temporarily without a job.

Wool manufactures, in sharp contrast with cotton, are mainly dependent on the home market which absorbed about two-thirds of the output in the pre-war years. Indeed they have accounted for an ever-diminishing proportion of total British exports over the past three centuries. The proportion was as high as two-thirds in the middle of the seventeenth century, and it was still almost one-half in the early eighteenth century, then it sank to one-sixth in the early nineteenth century, one-thirteenth in the early twentieth century, and one-seventeenth on the eve of the second world war. This relative decline denoted that other branches of the national economy had forged ahead in the export trade; there was no absolute decline in the volume of woollen and worsted exports as a whole and the proportion of operatives engaged on export work

---

[1] It is estimated that between 1912 and 1939 the average *ad valorem* duty payable abroad on a 16 oz. British cloth rose by 139 per cent. without taking account of various surcharges and additional taxes.

remained high. In spite of the fact that foreign competitors—
France and Germany—entered the field against her, England
more than held her own. The prognostication uttered so
frequently in the course of her economic history—that tariffs
and competition foreshadowed the eclipse of English oversea
trade—was signally falsified. Exports in 1912 exceeded those
of France and Germany together; their quantity was even
higher than in a notable year 1872, when owing to the Franco-
Prussian war external rivalry was largely negligible.

Between the two world wars, while England maintained and
even extended her share of international trade, it was a share of
a dwindling total because the crucial feature of the thirties was
an overwhelming fall in the volume of products exchanged
between nations. The trend away from the international
division of labour towards autarky, or self-sufficiency, began
during the first world war when the warring countries were
unable to supply the requirements of their former customers;
it received a powerful stimulus from the great depression of
1929–33. On an increasing scale every state sought to build up
its own industries, and this affected the demand for English
wool manufactures. England exported two-fifths of world
exports of wool tissues alike in 1928 and in 1938, but world
exports in 1938 were only half of 1928. The chief exporters of
wool—Australia, New Zealand, South Africa, Argentina and
Uruguay—doubled their home consumption of wool during
these ten years (1928–38), though New Zealand and South
Africa continued to provide growing markets for English wool
tissues. The markets in the Far East crashed when their
demand fell from 18 million lb. in 1928 to $2\frac{1}{2}$ millions a decade
later. Significant was the trend towards an expanding proportion of Empire consumption of English wool tissues. It rose
from one-eighth in the seventies to two-fifths before the first
world war, and approached one-half prior to the second world
war; the United States, formerly one of the principal markets,
dropped to one-twentieth. It is said that the cloths exported
abroad are in general of better quality than those sold on the
home market; yet the export trade is not confined to high-class
cloths; and, apart from finished products, it also comprises

intermediate products (tops, noils, yarns, shoddy) together with the by-products of wool fats: these intermediate and by-products have been as high as two-fifths in value of the total. The marketing of exports is in the hands of manufacturers[1] and merchants, the division corresponding largely to the nature of the market. Merchants order goods either in advance according to sample or upon receipt of actual instructions transmitted by agents abroad.

We must next glance at wool textiles in other leading countries.

The beginnings of a cloth manufacture in America can be traced back to the opening decades of the seventeenth century, for many of the early settlers in the plantations had been clothiers at home. At the end of the century the English government observed with concern that New England and other northern colonies were applying themselves 'too much' to the improvement of woollen fabrics amongst themselves. The problem of preventing the colonies from developing their own manufactures was a constant pre-occupation with the authorities at home, and wool textiles figured prominently in the category of industries that were frowned upon. Not content, however, to rely upon her superior economic efficiency the mother country embarked upon a policy of repressive legislation. Accordingly Parliament enacted (in 1699) that no raw wool, yarn or fabric, 'being the product or manufacture of any of the English plantations in America,' should be exported from the colonies or even transported from one colony to another: 'and we have since understood [so the Commissioners for Plantations reported the next year] that the said restraint has had a very good effect.' The sequel afforded an instructive example of the futility of harsh measures. A few years later the Commissioners were constrained to admit that notwithstanding the prohibition the northern colonies 'do not only clothe themselves with woollen goods, but furnish the same commodity to the more southern plantations.' Shortly before the War of Independence the governor of New York wrote: 'The custom

---

[1] In 1940–41 the manufacturers' share of exported cloth was 60 per cent.

of making coarse cloth in private families prevails throughout the entire province, and in almost every house a sufficient quantity is manufactured for the use of the family.'

The first factory in the United States came into existence subsequent to the Revolution at Hartford (Connecticut in New England). The equipment comprised looms, fulling mills and finishing machinery, and so enabled cloth to be manufactured in all its stages; but the venture proved short-lived (1788-1797). The real start of the American woollen industry on modern lines is associated with two brothers, English mechanics named Schofield, who migrated to the United States in 1793. They are credited with the first attempt to manufacture wool by power-driven machinery. They erected their factory in Massachusetts and others soon sprang up. Nevertheless as late as 1810 it was officially estimated that the cloth made in country districts was preponderately household cloth, that is, the spinning and weaving were done in the home. The nascent industry was stimulated by the war of 1812, which interrupted the trade between England and the United States and gave native manufacturers an opportunity to capture the domestic market. Their efforts were assisted by the fact that the introduction of merino sheep provided them with superior qualities of raw material. However after the war the importation of English woollens was resumed; and this seemed likely to check, at any rate temporarily, any further advance of the home industry. In these circumstances the demand for protective tariffs on imported woollens grew clamorous. An import duty—one-eighth of the value—had been imposed in 1789; it was now (1816) doubled; while a few years later (1824) it was raised to one-third. The policy of building up a native manufacture behind tariff walls met with strenuous opposition from the cotton growers. There was a cleavage of interests between the planters of the south, who supported free trade, and the manufacturers of the north. The former exported cotton and were apprehensive lest 'this and other agricultural industries would be destroyed for the emolument of the few.' The Agricultural Society of South Carolina protested (1827) that protective tariffs 'in favour of domestic manufactures at the expense of agriculture were pregnant with evil to southern interests.' At the moment the protest was unavailing since the next year the tariff mounted to one-half. Later southern resistance proved more successful and the tariff was again reduced to a quarter, but the struggle persisted with fluctuating fortunes; the duty levied in 1867 was said to amount 'nearly to prohibition of entry.' The innumerable and bewildering changes in the tariff system impressed upon the American woollen industry a speculative character which militated against steady and ordered progress.

Even more detrimental was the cleavage between the wool manufacturers and the wool growers. We have spoken elsewhere[1] of the Syracuse Convention (1865) in which an effort was made to reconcile their conflicting interests. The president of the National Association of Wool Manufacturers declared that 'neither can long prosper unless the other prospers also.' The manufacturers wanted protection against fabricated materials—'England draws her life from abroad; she returns to foreign markets the fruits of her labours.' The growers wanted protection against raw materials. Each side was powerful enough to secure what it wanted, and each gained a Pyrrhic victory. The manufacturers are protected against foreign competitors—but not against native competitors who produce fabrics made of other and cheaper materials. The growers are protected against foreign competitors—but they cannot hinder manufacturers from blending virgin wool with re-worked wool, cotton and rayon; thereby diminishing their dependence on costly home-grown wool. It may be partially owing to the high cost of the raw materials that American manufacturers are confined to the home market, where they are protected against the icy blast of external competition. They have signally failed to build up markets abroad, and exports of woollens are negligible.[2]

As in England, woollen and worsted factories in the United States are located mainly in the north-east section of the country.

[1] See Part I.
[2] Exports increased after the second world war, to meet the pressing needs of countries affected by the war. The percentage of production exported abroad rose from ·1 (1939) to 1·3 (1948) and fell to ·6 (1950).

They are concentrated in New England and the middle Atlantic states (New York, New Jersey and Pennsylvania), which absorb all but one-seventh.[1] The number of mills (according to the census of production in 1935) was 369 woollen and 226 worsted; the corresponding figures for the number of workers were 68,000 and 91,000. The worsted industry has a smaller number of plants coupled with a greater number of workers as well as a higher value of product. Its growth was due partly to changes in fashion which caused the demand for heavy woollens to decline relatively, and partly to the invention of mechanical combing which superseded the expensive manual process. Its structural organization follows the English pattern of specialization: some mills only comb, some only spin, some only weave. In marked contrast the typical woollen mill is integrated: it combines all processes—preparatory, spinning, weaving and finishing. One feature of interest is that woollen yarn in the United States is spun by the ring spinning-frame instead of the mule (as in England). This method diminishes labour costs and increases productivity, though the mule yields a finer thread.

A comparison of the productivity and earnings of labour in the wool textiles of the United States with those of England must take account of several things. Firstly, English cloth is superior in quality and costs less to manufacture. Secondly, the proportion of men (and therefore the output per head) is higher in the United States. Thirdly, England exports also intermediate products (tops, yarn, etc.). Yet when due allowance has been made for these factors, there still remain substantial differences in the earnings and output of labour which are both much greater in the United States. The phenomenon, however, is not confined to wool textiles but is characteristic of industry as a whole. England's ability to compete in world markets depends primarily upon the quality of her products, and any changes which increased output at the expense of quality would be detrimental to her long-term

[1] Of recent years there has been a marked trend away from the old-established wool textiles districts of New England and the mid-Atlantic states to the southern states.

interests. Subject to this paramount consideration there is doubtless considerable room for a wider adoption of improved technical methods.

French industry shares one feature in common with English industry: it is located mainly in the north-east corner of the country. In other respects it is widely dissimilar. England leads the world in the manufacture of worsteds for men's wear, while France enjoys supremacy in soft materials for women's wear. The contrast is due to differences in the technical processes. English worsteds are woven from hard yarn spun on the frame; French worsteds are woven from soft yarn containing less twist and spun on the mule. The preference for mule spinning in the French worsted industry arises from the fact that the latter uses wool of a shorter staple than English 'combing' wool—and the mule can handle short weak wool which could not bear the strain of the frame. Formerly worsteds were made from 'combing' wool and woollens from 'clothing' wool; the distinction was based on the length of the fibre whether it was more or less than $2\frac{1}{2}$ inches. However the distinction tended to be obliterated when machinery was devised[1] which could comb the shorter staples and so made them available for worsteds. Owing to this French (or Continental) system of manufacturing worsted yarn, merino wool—the finest in quality but usually the shortest in length—is no longer confined to woollens but can now be used for worsteds. When worsted yarn is made from short wool it undergoes the process of carding. The purpose is not to blend the fibres (as in the case of woollen carding), but to separate the fibres in preparation for combing which arranges them in parallel order. Finally it may be observed that the displacement of hand-looms by power-looms has been a slower process in France than in England. In the first decade of our century the former still numbered one-fourth of the total; sometimes looms in the homes were run by electric power. The survival of manual processes is one of the reasons for French pre-eminence in artistic woollen fabrics, since the skill of the hand-loom weaver can be more readily applied to changing fashions than can the machine. The organization of the rural

[1] An adaptation of Heilmann's combing machine.

N

industry in France reproduced the features of the English domestic system; the household weavers were supplied with yarn and returned the woven fabric.

Japan occupied an exceptional position. She relied almost exclusively upon imported wool; furthermore she came late into the field. Her emergence as a wool manufacturing country was in the years 1928–35; at a time when exports of woollen fabrics from England diminished by a third and those from Europe as a whole by a half, Japan multiplied her exports over eightfold.[1] Her speciality was light worsted cloth for tropical wear. Her wool consumption increased twenty-fivefold as compared with the years preceding the first world war, though the greater part of her industrial output went to meet the home demand stimulated by the adoption of European fashions and a rising standard of living. Modern methods of factory organization, coupled with up-to-date machinery, gave Japan an opportunity both to satisfy domestic needs and enter into the sphere of international competition.

[1] 1928—2½ million square yards; 1935—21·3 m.

APPENDIX

Geographical Distribution in England

WHILE THE COTTON industry has always been in the main associated with a single county, the woollen and worsted industries were formerly carried on in every part of the realm—although even in the middle ages certain areas became pre-eminent as the 'manufacturing districts' of England, namely, the west country, East Anglia and Yorkshire.

In early times the towns were the centres of cloth-making. Huntingdon, Lincoln, London, Nottingham, Oxford, Winchester and York had each its own gild of weavers in the twelfth century. Other important places were Bristol where one-fifth of the townsfolk were connected with the cloth trade, Colchester, Leicester, Northampton and Stamford; at Bury St. Edmunds the fullers were enjoined by the cellarer of the abbey to 'furnish cloth for his salt, otherwise he would prohibit them the use of the waters.' Worsted cloth was made at Worstead and Aylsham in Norfolk: Norwich, destined to become the metropolis of the worsted world, originally traded in leather and leather goods.

In the course of centuries the textile manufactures overflowed from the towns into the suburbs and country districts, where they developed free from any impediment or restraint. This trend away from the ancient boroughs to new industrial seats was in part, no doubt, prompted by the desire to evade the control of the craft gilds and escape financial obligations, but it was ultimately due to the natural growth of industry. Nevertheless the corporate towns did not surrender their privileged position without a struggle. They endeavoured as much as possible to retain in their own hands the sole right to make cloth; and they invoked in support of their claims the charters bestowed upon them by the Crown in the twelfth century, which gave them a practical monopoly within a large area. At first their monopoly was not seriously contested; and when town clothiers gave out work to country weavers the municipal authorities took steps to check the practice in order to protect urban craftsmen from the 'foreign' competition of rural artisans. However in the sixteenth century the villages ceased to depend upon the towns for industrial employment; and, owing to the rapid extension of the woollen manufacture in rural districts, the control over it began to slip from the grasp of the older boroughs. Thus in Yorkshire the prosperity of the corporate towns waned and their place was usurped by their younger rivals, the new country 'townlets' which owed their rise to the expansion of the textile industries. In 1561 the authorities of York—which in the middle ages was the greatest centre of weaving in the north—complained of the decayed fortunes of their city. 'The cause of the decay of the weavers and looms for woollen cloth within the city, as I do understand and learn, is the lack of cloth-making in the city as was in old time accustomed, which is now increased and used in the towns of Halifax, Leeds and Wakefield: for that not only the commodity of the water mills is there nigh at hand but also the poor folk as spinners, carders and other necessary workfolk for the weaving may there beside their hand-labour have rye, fire [fuel] and other relief good cheap, which is in this city very dear and wanting.' Yet it was not alone the presence of water mills and the cheapness of living which attracted artisans into the rural districts; even more important was the absence or at any rate the difficulty of supervision. The villages were left to a large extent unregulated, a circumstance which contributed to the disadvantages to which the older towns were exposed. In Yorkshire, for instance, the country weavers made cloth 'with woof of flocks,' a practice afterwards prohibited by Parliament. The oppressive ordinances of craft gilds concerning the fees of apprentices and admission to master-ship must have operated in the same direction.

The struggle between the established seats of industry and villages which were growing into towns constitutes one of the main economic movements of the sixteenth century. The former sought by means of legislative action to check the spread of manufactures, and to repress the activities of the new industrial

centres that were springing up around them. The celebrated
Weavers' Act (1555) laid down the principle that henceforth
'no person whatsoever, which heretofore hath not used or
exercised the feat, mistery or art of cloth-making, shall make
or weave any kind of broad white woollen cloths but only in a
city, borough, town corporate or market town or else in such
place or places where such cloths have been used to be commonly made by the space of ten years.' None the less the Tudor
monarchy was powerless to divert the tide of economic change
which was transforming mediaeval conditions and for good or
evil ushering in the modern world. At the opening of the seventeenth century the Venetian envoy in London wrote that broadcloth 'and especially kersies are made all over the kingdom in
the small hamlets and villages and not in the big towns only.'
The distribution of the wool textiles under the Early Stuarts
is roughly indicated in Fuller's list:

East:	(1)	Norfolk—Norwich fustians;
	(2)	Suffolk—Sudbury baize;
	(3)	Essex—Colchester says and serges;
	(4)	Kent—Kentish broadcloth.
West:	(1)	Devonshire—kersies;
	(2)	Gloucestershire—cloth;
	(3)	Worcestershire—cloth;
	(4)	Wales—Welsh friezes.
North:	(1)	Westmorland—Kendal cloth;
	(2)	Lancashire—Manchester cotton;
	(3)	Yorkshire—Halifax cloth.
South:	(1)	Somersetshire—Taunton serges;
	(2)	Hampshire—cloth;
	(3)	Berkshire—cloth;
	(4)	Sussex—cloth.

'Observe we here,' adds Fuller, 'that mid-England—Northamptonshire, Lincolnshire and Cambridge—having most of
wool, have least of clothing therein.'

    The main source of information for the eighteenth century is
Defoe's *Tour of Great Britain*, which covers the years 1724–1727.

In addition there are occasional notices in the works of Arthur
Young, Eden, and various topographical writers. The natural
starting-point of an industrial itinerary is Norfolk, which is
described by Defoe in the following terms. 'When we come into
Norfolk we see a face of diligence spread over the whole country;
the vast manufactures carried on (in chief) by the Norwich
weavers employ all the country round in spinning yarn for
them; besides many thousand packs of yarn which they receive
from other counties, even from as far as Yorkshire and Westmorland. This [eastern] side of Norfolk is very populous and
thronged with great and spacious market towns more and
larger than any other part of England so far from London,
except Devonshire and the West Riding of Yorkshire. Most of
these towns are very populous and large; but that which is
most remarkable is that the whole country round them is so
interspersed with villages, and those villages so large and full
of people.' Of this busy hive of industry the thriving centre was
Norwich, once the metropolis of East Anglia and the leading
manufacturing town in England. The staple products were
worsted stuffs, crapes and camlets made from the long-stapled
wool of Lincolnshire and Leicestershire. The wool produced
in Norfolk itself was not used at home but was sent to
Yorkshire, where it was carded and spun into cloth. The county
of Suffolk was associated with textiles from remote times. The
mass of its population was occupied in the preliminary branches
of the worsted industry, wool-combing and yarn-making, for
the manufacturers of Norwich in particular drew from Suffolk
their supplies of yarn. In Essex the most important town was
Colchester renowned for making bays and says.

Norfolk, Suffolk and Essex were 'famed for industry' yet
another part of East Anglia—Cambridgeshire—had 'no manufacture at all, nor are the poor except the husbandmen famed
for anything so much as idleness and sloth to their scandal be
it spoken.' This unfavourable estimate may be qualified by the
fact that the county possessed the greatest commercial mart in
the whole kingdom, Stourbridge Fair near Cambridge. A part
of the fair, known as the Duddery, was set apart for dealers in
the cloth trade; and the booths or tents, which were grouped

together in the form of a square, were so immense that they gave
the impression of another Blackwell Hall. Large quantities of
wool were also sold, especially the wool raised in Lincolnshire
where the longest staple was found. The buyers were chiefly
drawn from Norfolk, Suffolk and Essex whose industry demanded the long 'combing' wool.

In the early middle ages the economic condition of Kent was
in advance of most English counties. Lambard, in his *Perambula-
tion of Kent* written in 1576, declared that its artificers excelled
as makers of coloured woollen cloths, and that from them was
'drawn both sufficient store to furnish the wear of the best sort
of our own nation at home, and great plenty also to be transported to other foreign countries abroad.' In the sixteenth
century Kent received a large incursion of alien weavers particularly at Sandwich; and in the next century Fuller declared
that 'clothing is as vigorously applied here as in any other place,
and Kentish cloth at the present keepeth up the credit thereof
as high as ever before.' None the less Kent was unable to maintain its position among the manufacturing districts of England,
and under the Hanoverians it was numbered with Hampshire,
Leicestershire, Lincolnshire, Northamptonshire, Surrey and
Sussex among the counties which were not employed 'in any
considerable woollen manufacture.'

We now turn to the west country, the seat of the broadcloth
manufacture upon which the fame of English industry rested
down to the era of the 'Industrial Revolution.' At Painswick on
the way towards Stroud, as a traveller wrote in 1681, 'you
begin to enter the land of the clothiers who in these bourns
building fair houses because of the conveniency of water, so
useful for their trade, do extend their country some miles.' The
heart of the west country was 'the low flat country full of rivers
and towns and infinitely populous,' comprising part of Somersetshire, Wiltshire and Gloucestershire, and stretching from
Cirencester in the north to Sherborne in the south and from
Devizes in the east to Bristol in the west. The area extended
'about fifty miles in length where longest and twenty miles in
breadth where narrowest,' and it contained innumerable
market towns whose inhabitants were engaged in the woollen

manufacture. 'The River Avon waters this whole fruitful vale and the water seems particularly qualified for the use of clothiers, for dyeing the best colours and for fulling and dressing the cloth, so that the clothiers generally plant themselves upon this river.'

Among the manufacturing counties Gloucestershire held a foremost place: 'famous not for the finest cloths only but for dyeing those cloths of the finest scarlets and other grain colours that are anywhere in England.' It owed its pre-eminence, in part, to the quantity of sheep covering the downs and plains of Dorsetshire, Wiltshire and Hampshire (although, as the home-grown supply proved insufficient for its needs, it came to draw upon the midlands—Leicestershire, Lincolnshire and Northamptonshire—and even upon Ireland and Spain); and in part also to the 'excellent water' of the Stroud which was said to have a peculiar quality for dyeing scarlets. The county was covered, in Leland's picturesque phrase, with a network of 'clothing towns' and 'clothing villages.' Among the chief centres Defoe enumerates Cirencester 'populous and rich, full of clothiers.' Wiltshire and Somersetshire ranked with Gloucestershire as great industrial districts of the west country. In Wiltshire the most important town was Bradford. Somersetshire contained Taunton and Frome, while Bath was at one time associated with a woollen article known as Bath beaver.

The county of Devon was 'the largest and most populous in England, Yorkshire excepted.' It was 'so full of great towns and those towns so full of people and those people so universally employed in trade and manufactures, that not only it cannot be equalled in England but perhaps not in Europe.' Its original industry was the manufacture of kersies (narrow woollen cloth), and Devonshire kersies were the boast of Devonshire writers. 'Here are made the best and finest of the kingdom, which obtaineth to the inhabitants wealth, to the merchants traffic, and glory to the nation.' After the Revolution kersies were displaced by serges of which the warp was made with combed yarn and the weft with carded yarn. Among the seats of Devonshire wool textiles two held pride of place—Exeter and Tiverton.

The history of the West Riding of Yorkshire is remarkable in many ways. The records of its woollen industry stretch back to remotest times, yet for centuries the manufacture was in a backward condition. Even when the same quality of wool was imported from other parts of England, Yorkshire was unable to produce the same quality of cloth as the west country. The superiority of the latter was attributed to more careful sorting of the wool, improved methods of dyeing and finishing, and greater specialization. The West Riding sent abroad vast quantities but supplied markets like Russia and Poland, which took coarse fabrics to clothe their armies. The general level of the industry as regards quality and skill was a low one. The manufacturers gained an evil notoriety for their use of lamb's wool, flocks and other prohibited materials; and legislation was powerless to turn them from their malpractices. The estimation in which Yorkshire cloth was held in the seventeenth century may be gauged from Fuller's castigation: 'As I am glad to hear that plenty of a coarser kind of cloth is made in this county at Halifax, Leeds and elsewhere, whereby the meaner sort are much employed and the middle sort enriched, so I am sorry for the general complaints made thereof; insomuch that it is become a general by-word "to shrink as northern cloths" (a giant to the eye and dwarf in the use thereof) to signify such who fail their friends in deepest distress depending on their assistance. Sad that the sheep, the emblem of innocence, should unwillingly cover so much craft under the wool thereof; and sadder that fullers commended in Scriptures for making cloth white should justly be condemned for making their own consciences black by such fraudulent practices.' However in the eighteenth century the dormant energies of the north were quickened to new life. Its people now took upon themselves to wrest from East Anglia and the west country their industrial supremacy over the rest of England.

The staple industry of Yorkshire in remoter times was the manufacture of a narrow woollen cloth called kersey. A new page in the history of the county was opened up with the introduction of worsted cloth. The date to be assigned to this event is the end of the seventeenth century. The fact that Yorkshire

exported yarn to Norwich may well have suggested to Yorkshire men the possibility of working up the yarn at home and
entering into competition with Norfolk manufacturers; and the
fact that labour was apparently cheaper in the north made the
experiment feasible. The progress of the industry was at first
slow, but it brought the West Riding into rivalry with Norfolk
which had formerly enjoyed almost the sole monopoly of the
worsted trade; and in 1727 Defoe enumerated shalloons
(worsted cloth) along with broad woollen cloth and narrow
woollen cloth as 'the three articles of that country's labour.'
The challenge thrown down by Yorkshire to other industrial
centres began to attract attention early in the eighteenth
century. A writer in 1741 remarked: 'Yorkshire hath rivalled
them by under-working them, and very much decreased
their trade as also lowered their prices; they have also
robbed the west [country] and East [Anglia]; for I am told
they not only make long ells but bays in imitation of Bocking
bays, and sell them much cheaper for the reasons aforesaid.'
The success which attended the efforts of Yorkshire capitalists
to develop the worsted industry is shown by the value of the
worsted cloth made in the West Riding in 1772, which apparently equalled that made in Norwich. Nevertheless their
success was only partially achieved at the expense of the
Norwich trade, which embraced the finer qualities of worsted
while Yorkshire made the middle and lower qualities. Nor was it
due to the use of any machinery which at this date had not been
adopted in the worsted industry, even the fly shuttle being more
suitable at first for the making of broad woollen cloth.

In the eighteenth century a group of five towns constituted
the seat of 'that vast clothing trade by which the wealth and
opulence of this part of the country has been raised to what it
now is.' The five towns were Leeds, Halifax, Wakefield,
Huddersfield and Bradford. Leeds, 'a large wealthy and populous town,' was described by Thoresby in 1714 as 'deservedly
celebrated both at home and in the most distant trading parts
of Europe for the woollen manufacture.' It was renowned for
its cloth market which has been mentioned in another chapter.
The staple product was broadcloth although worsteds were

also made. The weavers of Halifax were mainly worsted weavers, and the town drove a great trade in kersies and shalloons, tammies, callimancoes and russets. Halifax preserved the right of beheading cloth-stealers and other thieves down to 1650, and a verse of the Beggars' Litany ran:

> From Hell, Hull and Halifax
> Good Lord deliver us!

Wakefield was known for its cloth market, which ranked second only to Leeds, as well as for cheapness of living—'A right honest man,' observed Leland in the reign of Henry VIII, 'shall fare well for twopence a meal.' The town specialized in cloth-finishing and here cloth was brought to be dyed and dressed. Huddersfield was 'another large clothing place;' but Bradford had not yet acquired the prominence which awaited the future metropolis of the worsted industry. The inhabitants were supposed to number about five thousand of whom two-thirds were employed in the manufacture of callimancoes, russets and other fabrics. The town's reputation for fraudulent work may be gauged from a verse in a Methodist hymn:

> On Bradford likewise look Thou down
> Where Satan keeps his seat.

The textile industry was not confined in Yorkshire to towns. The greater part of the domestic clothiers lived in villages or hamlets scattered over a district measuring twenty to thirty miles in length and twelve to fifteen miles in breadth. Their dispersed state was regarded by contemporaries as 'highly favourable to their morals and happiness;' and it was one of the criticisms against the factory system that it concentrated great masses of the industrial population within restricted urban areas. The classical description of the West Riding, with its continuous line of villages growing one into the other and linked up by innumerable hamlets and detached houses, is contained in Defoe's *Tour of Great Britain*. 'We found the country one continued village, hardly a house standing out of a speaking distance from another, and almost at every house there was a tenter and almost on every tenter a piece of cloth or kersey or shalloon, for they are the three articles of that country's labour. Among the manufacturers' houses are likewise scattered an infinite number of cottages or small dwellings in which dwell the workmen which are employed and the women and children, all of whom are always busy carding, spinning, etc. so that no hands being unemployed all can gain their bread even from the youngest to the ancient; hardly anything above four years old but its hands are sufficient to itself.'

We must not omit to mention other notable centres of wool textiles: Worcester, Coventry, Newbury, Bristol, Kendal, Rochdale and Manchester. An old historian of Worcester affirms that in the seventeenth century its manufacture of broadcloth was the most considerable of any town in the kingdom. Certainly as late as 1724 the town carried on 'a great share of the clothing trade,' and enjoyed the repute of making some of the best broadcloth. Coventry, 'a large and populous city [where] the timber houses project forward and towards one another till in the narrow streets they are ready to touch one another at the top,' drove a large trade in tammies.[1] Newbury, 'an ancient clothing town,' gloried in its association with England's most celebrated clothier John Winchcombe; but it had 'much declined' by the opening of the eighteenth century. The fame of Bristol cloth under the Tudors is reflected in Skelton's description of a gay dress: 'Her kyrtle was of Bristowe red.' Kendal in Westmorland obtained a reputation for the manufacture of Kendal cottons, a coarse narrow cloth made not from cotton but from Westmorland wool. Of the Lancashire towns once connected with woollen goods, particular interest attaches to Rochdale which still retains the connexion. In 1778 it was described as 'famous for manufactories of cloth, kersey and shalloon. Every considerable house is a manufactory, and is supplied with a rivulet or little stream without which the business cannot be carried on. The women and children all employed here, not a beggar or idle person being to be seen.' In former days Manchester, now the metropolis of the cotton industry, was also a seat of the woollen industry. 'It excels,' wrote Camden in 1590, 'the towns immediately around it in

[1] Fine worsted cloth.

handsomeness, populousness, woollen manufacture, church and college, but did much more excel them in the last age by the glory of its woollen cloths which they call Manchester cottons.'

The 'Industrial Revolution' had remarkable effects upon the geographical distribution of the woollen and worsted industries. Instead of being carried on throughout the realm in innumerable towns, villages and hamlets as in past centuries, they are now concentrated mainly in the West Riding of Yorkshire. In East Anglia, once its chief seat, the worsted trade is practically extinct; the west country, the ancient seat of the broadcloth trade, still makes the finest woollen cloth; but over both alike may be written the epitaph 'Ichabod.' This migration of industry was the outcome of various factors; and it would be a mistake to regard the introduction of machinery as the sole explanation of the growth of the West Riding, where industrial expansion preceded the advent of the factory system. Even before the days of machinery the early Yorkshire clothiers were boasting, not without justification, that 'in spite of fate [the woollen manufactures would] come into these northern counties.'

The decline of Norwich as the focus of the worsted world is generally attributed to Yorkshire's natural advantages, namely coal and iron; but Norwich had one great asset in its favour— the reputation of its fabrics due to the ingenuity of its manufacturers coupled with the inherited skill of its weavers; and after all, coal and iron could have been imported despite the higher costs. Among the causes responsible for the decay of the Norwich trade three may be singled out for mention. First: the Norwich manufacturers displayed marked enterprise in the invention of new fabrics, and in this way endeavoured to overcome the ruinous effects of the American and French wars; yet their fabrics were soon imitated in Yorkshire, 'made in an inferior manner' (as it was alleged) 'and substituted at a cheaper rate.' Thus in the last years of the eighteenth century the mainstay of Norwich was the manufacture of worsted camlets[1] for

---

[1] Camlet was light worsted cloth made of long wool hard spun, but formerly made of the hair of Angora goat.

the East India Company. After the latter lost its monopoly of trade with India (1813) and China (1833), Yorkshire proceeded to export to Eastern markets an inferior imitation which did its Norwich rivals 'very great injury.' It was the cheapness of Yorkshire cloth, combined with a very colourable imitation of the original, that enabled the West Riding to gain command over the markets at home and abroad. Changes in fashion also told in favour of Yorkshire where light stuffs were made with cotton warps of which supplies were close at hand. Second: the Norwich manufacturers failed to keep pace with the north in regard to machinery. As late as 1839 Norwich contained but a handful of power-looms in one of its mills; whereas four years before, according to the returns made by the factory inspectors, Yorkshire contained 2,856 worsted power-looms. The difficulty of competing with Yorkshire in these circumstances proved insuperable especially since the Norwich weavers, owing to their superior organization, resisted reductions of wages with more success than their Yorkshire fellows. Third: the failure to introduce machinery in spinning may be connected with the fact that Norwich was not dependent on local supplies of yarn and therefore lacked the inducement to promote the new methods of spinning. The first yarn factory was not set up until 1834, and it was then too late to overcome the advantages which Yorkshire now enjoyed—the possession of coal and iron in close proximity; the practical monopolization of the combing processes, against which it was impossible to compete without the erection of costly machinery; and finally the existence of a large foreign demand for Yorkshire yarn, which made the outlay of capital in the north a profitable venture. For these various reasons Yorkshire forged completely ahead; it had in 1850 no less than 746,000 spindles—forty times the number in Norfolk.

We have seen that the migration of industry from East Anglia to the West Riding was not due primarily, as is commonly supposed, to the possession of iron and coalfields though these were important elements in the situation. It was the inability of the old-established seats to adapt themselves to the altered economic conditions, which enabled their younger and more enterprising rival to outstrip them in the race for industrial pre-eminence. Just as the older English boroughs proved unable in the sixteenth century to retain their ascendancy because their structure failed to keep pace with the changing needs of the time, so in the nineteenth century industry migrated to those districts which showed the greatest power of adaptability to the new order. The reasons for the fatal delay in the introduction of machinery both in the eastern and western counties of England are twofold: firstly the conservatism of the workers, who claimed a vested interest in their occupation and were able to prevent or at any rate retard the use of machines which destroyed this vested interest; and secondly the want of an enterprising spirit on the part of the manufacturers, who lacked the stimulus which the proximity of the Lancashire cotton industry supplied to Yorkshire to discard the traditional organization of wool textiles and develop them—with the aid of machinery—on the lines of the factory system. 'While the men of Leeds and Huddersfield,' wrote a hand-loom commissioner in 1839, 'were constantly in their mills and taking their meals at the same hours as their workpeople the clothiers of Gloucestershire, some of them, were indulging in the habits and mixing with the "gentle blood" of the land.'

The west country had water-power in abundance as well as easy access to the coalfields;[1] yet neither one nor the other served to prevent the gradual decay of its woollen manufacture. Worcester for example boasted its streams, it was close to the Staffordshire coalfields, and a navigable river led to the Bristol Channel; nevertheless the Worcester clothiers let their opportunities pass by and weakly succumbed. A pamphlet written in 1800 attributed this decline of the west country to the fact that 'Yorkshire manufacturers can with much greater facility introduce machinery than we can in the west of England. The opposition that we generally meet with in introducing machinery is so great that until the Yorkshire manufacturers have stolen the article away from us, we are almost afraid to introduce it.' We have mentioned the difficulties which attended the employment of the fly shuttle in the western counties, and the

[1] Coal, of course, was cheaper in Yorkshire.

spinning jenny received an equally hostile reception provoking riots at Shepton Mallet in Somersetshire in 1776. In each case the opposition subsequently died down, but the delay enabled Yorkshire to reap the first-fruits of the new inventions and to consolidate its position. A clothier at Shepton Mallet has given evidence of the resistance which he encountered in adopting improved methods. 'I have upon introducing machinery been obliged to apply to government for military protection. I would introduce machines that I do not now make use of but for the great opposition I know I must meet with from the labouring manufacturers.' Thus in the long struggle of the north of England to wrest industrial supremacy from the east and the west, the 'Industrial Revolution' assured it the final victory largely on account of the comparative ease with which machinery was introduced.

During the past hundred years Yorkshire has not only maintained but has strengthened its ascendancy in the wool textile industry. In the middle of the nineteenth century barely two-thirds of the operatives were concentrated in this area; between the two world wars the proportion had risen to four-fifths. Other parts of the kingdom are now restricted to one-tenth of the worsted section and to one-third of the woollen section—for the west of England and Scotland continue to produce high quality cloth. To-day, as in former times, there is specialization in all districts: thus Bradford, Halifax and Keighley are associated with worsteds, Huddersfield with superior worsteds and woollens, Dewsbury and Batley with cheap woollens, Witney with blankets, the Hebrides with Harris tweed.

Bibliographical Note

The sources utilized in this book comprise my *Economic History of England* Volumes I–III (A. & C. Black Ltd) and my *History of the Woollen and Worsted Industries* (A. & C. Black Ltd), together with the comprehensive Reports issued by the United States Tariff Commission and the United Kingdom Board of Trade *Working Party Report: Wool*, as well as numerous monographs (including J. Klein, *The Mesta*, Harvard University Press). The *Wool Digest* published by the International Wool Secretariat contains current statistical data. (It may be noted that estimates of sheep and wool production are liable to subsequent revision). A detailed bibliography of the English cloth manufacture will be found in the Appendix to my *History of the Woollen and Worsted Industries*.

Index

Abb, 124
Abingdon, 58, 76
Abingdon Abbey, 76
Act of Parliament, *1337*–57; *1390*–15;
 1489–104; *1495*–159; *1497*–113;
 1532–119; *1551*–159; *1554*–15, 67,
 119; *1667*–99, 101; *1696*–24; *1698*–
 24; *1699*–102, 173; *1700*–100; *1707*–
 103; *1719*–98; *1721*–101; *1726*–115;
 1736–101; *1788*–29, see also Flannel
 Act, Manchester Act, Statute of
 Apprentices, Weavers' Act
Adam and Eve, 49, 83
Addingham, 156
Africa
— north, 36
— south, 4, 8, 37, 38, 39, 42–3, 172
— statistics, 38, 43
African Company, 95
Agrarian Revolution, 11
Agricultural labourers, 164
Agricultural Society of South Carolina,
 174
Alfonso the Learned, 37
Alfred, King, 55
Aliens
— immigrants, 57–62, 183
— merchants, 17–19, 52
Alpaca, 4
Alsace, 144
America
— north see United States
— south, 5, 8, 37, 38, 42 see also Argen-
 tina and Uruguay
Angora goat, 4, 189
Antwerp, 3, 75
Apprentices, 57–8, 63–4, 67–8, 82–3,
 91–2, 113–14, 117, 166, 180
Aragon, 37
Arden, 17, 18
Argentina, 4, 38, 41–2, 44, 172
— statistics, 38, 42
Arkwright, Richard, 132–8, 140, 142
Arras, 61
Arte della lana, 49
Arte di calimala, 49
Artois, 21
Assize of Cloth, 106, 166 see also Aul-
 nagers
Auctions, 7, 8, 9, 41
Aulnage, 107

Aulnagers, 93, 105–7
Australia, 4–6, 8–9, 31, 37–42, 44–5,
 155, 172
— fleece, weight of, 4
— statistics, 38, 40
— types of wool, 2
— wool, marketing of, 9
Autarky, 172
Avon, River, 184
Aylsham, 179

Bacon, Francis, 51, 103
Baines, Edward, 133
Baize, 120, 181
Bakewell, Robert, 32, 33
Bale, 6, 7
Balfour Committee, 150
Bastard, 12
Bath, 67, 77, 184
Bath-beaver, 184
Batley, 192
Batten, 125, 126, 130, 131
Bays, 61, 182, 186
Beam, 49, 125
Beard, 143, 146
Beaux Merchant, The, 80
Bedfordshire, 85
Beggars' Litany, 187
Benefit clubs, 114
Beni-Merines, 36
Bennett, Will, 112
Berkeley, 35
Berkshire, 181
Beverley, 56
Bible, The, 1, 49
'Big Ben', 143
Bills of Exchange, 19–20
Birmingham, 134
'Blackleg', 66
Blackwell Hall, 79, 93, 183
Blaize, Bishop, 66, 143
Blanket, 56, 192
Blanket, Thomas, 56, 72, 77
'Blue-nails', 50
Blundell, Peter, 73
Bobbin, 125, 133, 136, 140
Bocking, 186
Boer farmers, 43
Bolingbroke, Lord, 74
Bolivia, 4
Bolton, 135, 162

195

Bombazine, 120
Book of Proverbs, 83
Botany, 40
Botany Bay, 40
Bourne, Daniel, 137
Brabant, 21, 49, 58 see also Low Countries
Bradford (Wiltshire), 78, 81, 184
Bradford (Yorkshire), 143, 156, 158, 164–5, 171, 186–7, 192
Brayer, 118
Brian, Martin, a clothier, 77
Bristol, 58, 64, 72, 93, 179, 183, 188
Bristol Channel, 191
Britain see Great Britain
Britain, Roman, 55
British Commonwealth, 3, 8, 9, 31, 172 see also Colonies
British Merchant, The, 104
British Wool Marketing Board, 9
Broadcloth, 60, 61, 113, 131, 181, 183, 186, 188–9
Broggers, 16
Brokers, 7–9, 41 see also Factors
Bruges, 11, 16, 50
Burford, 76
Burlers, 69, 118 see also Burling
Burling, 127, 153
Bury St Edmunds, 179
Byland, 18

Calais, 19–21
Calicoes, 100–1
Callimanco, 120, 187
Cambridge, 182
Cambridgeshire, 85, 181–2
Camden, 51, 188
Camel, 4
Camlets, 51, 120, 182, 189
Canterbury, 22, 61, 73
Cap (spindles), 139, 149
Cape of Good Hope, 39, 43
Capitalism, 69, 113–14
Capitalists, 50, 69, 71–2, 78, 79, 87, 94, 103, 153, 157, 186 see also Clothiers
Capitalist system, 73, 108, 167
Carders see Wool-carders
Carding see Wool-carding
Carsays, 61
Carter, William, 22–4
Cartwright, Edmund, 141–4, 165
Cashmere, 4
Castile, 37
Catullus, 123
Cave (publisher), 134
Celys, 19
Chain, 85, 124

Chapman, a clothier, 77
Charles I, 22, 97
Charles II, 108
Charles the Great, 55
Chaucer, 67
Cheshire, 158
Child, Sir Josiah, 28, 106
Children, 54, 64, 75, 82–4, 86, 88–9, 90–1, 156, 158, 160, 164, 169, 188
— wages, 86, 90
China, 4, 100, 190
Cirencester, 11, 77, 183–4
Cistercians, 10, 18
Civil War, 27, 51, 98, 113
Cleveland, 17–18
Cloaks, 55
Cloth see Wool Textiles in England and Wool Textiles in Other Countries
Cloth-Dressers' Society, 116
Cloth-finishers, 87–8, 103, 116–17, 160, 170 see also Cloth-finishing, Dresser and Shearmen
Cloth-finishing, operations, 94, 130, 151, 158–9, 167, 170, 185, 187 see also Cloth-finishers, Dressing, Shearing frame and Shearmen
— trade unions, 116–17, 160
Clothiers, 11, 14–15, 24, 26, 69, 71–80, 82–3, 85, 88–95, 101, 103, 107–12, 115, 132, 152–3, 159, 166, 173, 180, 183–4, 187, 189, 191–2 see also Capitalists and Manufacturer
Clothier's Delight, The, 108
Cloth-stealers, 187
Cloth-workers, 75, 87
Cloth-working, 94 see also Cloth-finishing
Clove, 138
Coal and Iron, 189–91
Cockayne, Alderman, 103
Coggeshall, 56
Coke, Chief Justice, 51
Colchester, 56, 61, 132, 179, 181–2
Colonies, 97, 102, 173 see also British Commonwealth
Colting, 83
Combers see Wool-combers
Combing see Wool-combing
Comb-pot, 121, 143
Combs, 121
Commission basis, 8, 88, 167, 168 see also Brokers and Factors
Commissioners for Plantations, 25, 173
Commons, House of, see Parliament
Companies
— chartered, 95
— joint stock, 153, 168

Considerations on the East India Trade, 70
Cook, Captain, 41
Co-operative Association, 7, 8
'Cop the weft', 139
Coppus Cotenni, 17–18
Corriedale (sheep), 41
Cotswolds, 14, 16, 34
Cottage industry *see* Industry
Cotton, 4, 51, 100–1, 105, 130, 133–4,
    139, 142, 156, 158, 160–1, 170–1,
    174–5, 179, 188, 190–1
Count of yarn, 2
Coventry, 65, 188
Craft Gilds *see* Gilds
Craftsmanship, 57, 154
Crapes, 120, 182
Credit, 15, 19, 20, 64, 79, 93
Cromford, 137
Crompton, Samuel, 139, 140
Cromwell, Oliver, 22
Cromwell, Thomas, 76
Croppers, 87 *see also* Cloth-finishers
Croppers' ballad, 160
Croppers' Society, 116
Crossbred, 2, 3, Chapter 3, 167
Cullompton, 81
Customs revenue, 16 *see also* Tariffs
Cuthbert, a clothier, 77

Defoe, Daniel, 51, 74, 78, 89, 100,
    181–2, 184, 187
Deloney, Thomas, 74
'Descriptive of the Manners of the
    Clothiers', 91
Devizes, 183
Devonshire, 181–2, 184
Dewsbury, 192
Dimensions, statutory *see* Assize of
    Cloth
Dionysius Periegetes, 10
Distaff, 49, 54, 83–6, 122–4, 155
Dolman, Thomas, 76
Dolphin Holme, 156
Domesday Book, 35
Domestic manufacturer, 90–4, 153, 157
Domestic System, 49, 53, 68–94, 139,
    152, 166, 178
— defects, 88–90
— merits, 88, 92–3
Donisthorpe, 145
Dorset Down (sheep), 34
Dorsetshire, 184
Draperies, new, 61, 62
Drapers, 79, 101, 104
Drawer, 119, 130
Drawing process, 137
Dresser, master, 88, 94 *see* Cloth-finishers

Dressing, 154, 184 *see also* Cloth-
    finishing
Dressing machine, 157
Drop-box, 131
Druggets, 51, 120
Dryden, 10, 81
Duddery, 182
Duroy, 120
Dutch, 43, 58, 59, 61, 106 *see also* Low
    Countries
Dye-house, 75
Dyeing, 49, 54, 56, 91, 96, 103,
    107, 130, 151, 167, 184–5 *see also*
    Dyers
Dyer, *The Fleece*, 7, 119, 123, 126, 129,
    134, 154–5
Dyers, 58, 63, 65–7, 69, 72, 75, 88, 118
    see also Dyeing
Dyers' Hall, 96

Earle, Emma, 67
East Anglia, 179, 182, 185–6, 189, 190
East India Company, 100, 190
Eastland Company, 95
Eden, Sir William, 182
Edward III, 16, 57, 59, 60, 72
Edward IV, 17, 77
Edward VI, 12
Edward the Elder, 55
Elizabeth, Queen, 98
Ell, 56
Ell, long, 186
Ellman, John, 33
Embezzlement, 78, 89
Emigration of textile workers, 97–8
Employment, term of, 65, 111
England, 8, 37–9, 44, 96, 174–5
— sheep, Chapter 2, 54, 77, 184
— sheep (breeds), 32–4
— sheep (export of), 33, 36–8, 41–3
— sheep-farming (growth of), 10–14
— wool (exports: statistics), 31
— wool (history of), Chapter 2
— wool (imports: statistics), 31
— wool (marketing of), 9, 14–21
— wool (praise of), 1, 10, 16, 28, 32, 34
— wool (Spanish imported), 28, 31, 37
— wool textiles *see* Wool Textiles in
    England
'Enoch', 160
Essex, 22, 108, 181, 182, 183
Estamanes, 120
Exeter, 184
Exports *see under* Sheep, Wool *and* Wool
    Textiles
Exporters *see* Merchant exporters *and*
    Wool staplers

Fabyan, 55
Factories *see* Factory System
— size of, 167–8
Factors, 79, 80, 95–6 *see also* Brokers
Factory Inspector's Report, 153
Factory System, 54, 68–9, 72, 74–8, 90,
  139, 152, 154, 156, 166–8, 187, 191
Fairford, 11, 77
Fairs, 9, 182
Falkland Islands, 42
Far East, 172, 190
Farming, mixed, 5, 35, 44
Faversham, 22
Feeder, 137–8
Finishing *see* Cloth-finishing
Firwood, 140
Fitzherbert, 86
Flanders, 16, 21, 37, 49, 50, 56–8, 72,
  111 *see also* Low Countries
Flannel Act, 99
Fleece, The, by Dyer *see* Dyer
Fleece, weight of, 4
Fleece wool *see under* Wool
Flocks (refuse of wool), 105, 180, 185
Florence, 18, 49, 50
Flyer (spindles), 139, 149
Flyshuttle, 83, 86, 130–2, 152, 155,
  186, 191
Fold-soke, 35
Folkestone, 24
Forests, national, 5
Foster of Horbury, 159
Frame, 139, 149, 157, 170, 176–7
Frame-spinners, 170
France, 16, 21–4, 26–7, 37, 57, 98, 104,
  110, 132–3, 172
— wool, 45
— wool textiles, 177–8
Free Trade
— in cloth, 104, 174–5
— in wool, 16, 22, 27, 30, 104
Friezes, 58, 181
Friscobaldi, 18
Frome, 155, 184
Fuller, Thomas, 52, 58–9, 61, 74, 181,
  183, 185
Fullers, 58, 63, 65–6, 69, 72–3, 76, 88,
  118, 127, 179, 185 *see also* following
  items
Fuller's Field, 49
Fuller's pots, 128
Fulling, 49, 54, 127–9, 153, 184 *see also*
  Fullers *and* Fulling mill
Fulling mill, 75, 76, 105, 128–9, 131,
  155
Fustians, 101, 181
Futures market, 3

Gear, 125
Gennes, M. de, 141
George III, 30, 39
Germany, 26, 31, 37, 84, 98, 113, 172
Ghent, 11, 16, 67
Gig mills, 131, 158–9, 160, 166
Gilds, Craft, 37, 56, 59, 63–8, 113,
  179–80
Gild System, 53, 63, 68, 69
Gloucester, 66
Gloucestershire, 82, 112, 114, 130, 155,
  158–9, 181, 183–4, 191
Glue, 141
Gott, Benjamin, 152
Gower (poet), 16
Graziers, 11, 12–13, 26, 29, 53, 111 *see
  also* Sheepfarmers
Great Britain, 4, 39 *see also* England,
  Scotland, Wales

Halifax, 15, 77, 94, 164, 180–1, 185–7,
  192
Hampshire, 22, 67, 181, 183–4
Hampshire Down (sheep), 34
Hand-cards, 120–1, 137
Hand-loom *see* Looms
Hand-loom Commissioner's Report,
  163, 191
Hand-wheel, 123 *see also* Spinning-
  wheel
Hanks, 2
Hargreaves, James, 138–9, 140
Harris tweed, 192
Hartford, 174
Healds, 125
Hebrides, 192
Heilmann, Josué, 144–5, 177
Henry I, 56
Henry VII, 103
Henry VIII, 17, 77
Herrick (poet), 85
Hertfordshire, 85
Highlands (Scotland), 84, 128
Highs, Thomas, 132, 135–6
Hirst, a clothier, 159
Hodgkins, a clothier, 77
Hog's wool *see under* Wool
Holden, Isaac, 145–6
Holinshed, 73
— *see also* Shakespeare (110)
Holland, 21, 97–8, 110 *see also* Low
  Countries
'Homesteaders', 5
Horse-power, 137, 144, 156
Hosiery, 167
Hours of labour, 83, 86, 88–9, 154, 165,
  170

House of Commons *see* Parliament
Household cloth, 174
Housing conditions, 170
Huddersfield, 186–7, 191-2
Hull, 187
Hungary, 37
Huntingdon, 56, 179
Huskisson, 97

'Illegal' workmen, 82, 166
India, 4, 100, 190
— textiles, 99–101
'Industrial Revolution', 50, 69, 71, 79, 82, 161–2, 165, 183, 189, 192
Industry, cottage, 85, 88 *see also* Domestic System
Integration of Industry, 166–7, 176
Interlopers, 95
Inventions in wool textiles, 130–51
Ireland, 58, 66, 97
— wool, 23–5, 27–8, 184
— wool textiles, 101–2, 131
— emigrants, 164
Isle of Skye, 128
Italy, 16, 17, 123 *see also* Florence

Jack of Newbury *see* Winchcombe
James I, 22, 26, 98, 103
James II, 24
Japan
— wool, 45
— wool textiles, 178
Jenny *see* Spinning Jenny
Joint Organization stocks, 7
Journal to Stella, 74
Journeymen, 58, 63–4, 67–8, 77, 83, 91–3, 113, 117, 131
Judges, 113
Justices of the Peace, 109, 112
Juveniles, 169 *see also* Children

Kashmir, 4
Kay, clockmaker, 135–6
Kay, John, 83, 86, 130–2, 155
Kay, Robert, 131
Keighley, 164, 192
Kempe, John, 57, 72
Kendal, 77, 181, 188
Kendal cottons, 188
Kennedy, 140
Kent, 22, 25, 34, 181, 183
Kent, a clothier, 77
Kersies, 61, 65, 73–4, 181, 184–5, 187–8
Kingeswood, 35

Labour
— division of, 69–70
— earnings *see* Wages
— hours *see* Hours
— organization *see* Trade Unionism
— sweated, 86
Laissez-faire, 104, 106, 113, 166
Lambard, 10, 183
Lambs, 5, 36, 44
— lamb's wool *see under* Wool
Lancashire, 15, 86, 158, 181, 188, 191
Lancastrian dynasty, 60
Langland, 84, 127
Large-scale production, 167
Lastings, 120
Latimer, 12
Lavenham, 77
Leaf, 125
Leeds, 81, 86, 93, 94, 132, 180, 185–7, 191
Lees, John, 138
Leicester, 179
Leicesters (sheep), 33–4
Leicestershire, 15, 158, 182–4
Leigh, 135
Leland, 76, 77, 184, 187
Leominster, 14
Levant Company, 95
Lincoln, 56, 179
Lincolns (sheep), 34
Lincolnshire, 15, 56, 181–4
Linen, 101–2, 160–1
Lister, 145–6
London, 8, 9, 20, 25, 40, 56, 58, 61, 65, 67, 73–4, 79, 93, 95, 112, 129, 179, 181
Long wool *see under* Wool
Looms, 72, 74, 76–8, 80, 83, 86, 90–1, 111, 124–6, 131, 141, 143, 153, 155, 163, 166 *see also* Shuttle *and* Weaving
— automatic, 150
— broad, 83, 126, 131, 149, 155
— common, 131
— 'cut', 115
— double-handed, 131
— hand, 143, 152–3, 163, 177, defects of, 126–7, 131, 154
— makers, 64, 69, 80
— narrow, 126, 149
— number employed, 86, 111
— number of, 78, 80, 83, 91, 113, 158, 166, 190
— power, 127, 130, 141–3, 149–50, 152, 157–8, 163, 177, 190
— price, 80
— rented, 78
— spring, 131, 155

Low Countries, 49, 50, 57 *see also*
Brabant, Dutch, Flanders, Holland,
Netherlands, United Provinces
Luaghad, 128
Luccock, 7, 32–3, 130, 161
Luddite riots, 159

MacArthur, John, 39
Machinery, 6, 39, 57, 69, 90, 104, 117,
130–61, 167, 169, 174, 177–8, 186,
see also Looms (power), Spinning
machines, Wool-carding (machines),
Wool-combing (machines)
— benefits of, 153–4
— drawbacks, 154–5
— introduction, 129–30, 152–61, 164–5,
189–92
— inventions, 130–51
— opposition to, 129, 131–2, 153–61,
191–2
McKinley tariff, 171
Magna Carta, 106
Magnus Intercursus, 103
Maldon, 56
Malmesbury, 76
Malmesbury Abbey, 76
Manchester, 51, 77, 138, 141–2, 181,
188
Manchester Act (1736), 101
Manchester cottons, 189
Manufacturer of cloth, 4, 6, 9, 11, 14,
16, 22, 27–31, 90–4, 104, 153, 166–9,
173, 175, *see also* Clothiers *and* Domes-
tic manufacturer
— definition of, 71
Margaret, prioress, 17
Marketing
— cloth, 79–80, 91, 93–6, 168–9, 171,
173 *see also* Merchants *and under*
Wool Textiles in England (exports)
— market, public, 93–4, 182–3, 187
—wool, 6–9, 14–21, 41, 183 *see also*
Wool staplers *and under* Wool (exports)
Massachusetts, 174
Mass-production, 151
May, John, 105
Medley cloth, 130, 159
Merchant Adventurers, 94, 95, 103,
113
Merchant exporters, 79, 94, 95, 103
Merchants
— cloth, 79, 80, 88, 93–4, 106, 111–12,
119, 152–3, 167, 168, 173 *see* Merchant Adventurers *and* Merchant
exporters
— wool *see* Aliens *and* Wool staplers

Merchants of the Staple *see* Wool
staplers
Merino, 2, 3, 6, 7, 30, Chapter 3, 167,
174, 177
Mesta, 36–7
Methodist hymn, 187
Methuen Treaty, 104
Middlemen
— cloth *see* Factors, Merchants, Re-
tailers, Wholesalers
— wool *see* Wool staplers
Milan, 56
Milling (fulling), 127
Mills
— joint stock, 153
— public, 159
— woollen, 153, 167 *see also* Factories
Misselden, 28
Mohair, 4
Mokadoes, 61
Monasteries, 75–6
Monastic houses—sale of wool, 10, 17–18
Montgomeryshire, 158
More, Sir Thomas, 13
Motive power, 128, 154 *see also* Power
Mowsters, 96
Mule, 139, 140–1, 149, 150, 157, 176–7
— automatic, 141
— spinners, 170
Mun, Thomas, 53
Mungo, 4
Muslin, 162
Mutton, 32–4, 41, 43, 45
Mutton breeds, 33–4, 36, 38, 43

Naamah, 49
National Association of Wool Manu-
facturers, 175
National Farmers' Union Wool Mar-
keting Scheme, 9
National Forests, 5
Negretti, 30
Netherlands, 17, 58, 61, 103 *see also*
Low Countries
New Draperies *see* Draperies
Newbury, 74, 76, 188
New England, 173–4, 176
New Jersey, 176
New South Wales, 4, 39, 41
New York, 3, 173, 176
New Zealand, 4, 5, 8, 31, 34, 38, 41,
172
— statistics, 38, 41
— types of wool, 2
Nip machine, 145–6
Noble, James, 146–7
Noils, 121, 143, 145–6, 167, 173

Norfolk, 15, 33, 85, 97, 156, 158, 179, 181-3, 186, 190
Norman Conquest, 56
Northampton, 134, 179
Northamptonshire, 181, 183-4
Northumberland, 158
Norwich, 15, 58, 61, 66, 93, 113, 179, 181-2, 186, 189, 190
Nottingham, 65, 137, 179
Nottinghamshire, 116, 141

Offa, King, 55
Oil, 127
On England's Commercial Policy, 16
Osney Abbey, 76
Owlers, 23 see also under Wool (smuggling)
Oxford, 56, 76, 179
Oxford Down (sheep), 34

Pack-house, 85
Paddocks, 5
Painswick, 183
Papplewick, 156
Parliament, 16, 24-5, 51-2, 78, 97-9, 100, 101, 105, 107-8, 110, 113-15, 120, 160, 166, 180
— Oxford, 49, 56
Parter, 118
Partition Ordinance, 20
Paul, Lewis, 132-5, 137, 154
Pearked, 91
Pennant, Thomas, 127
Pennsylvania, 176
Persia, 100
Peru, 4
Phillip, Governor, 39
Picking peg, 131
Picks, 125, 127, 150, 152
Pictish Towers, 123
Piers the Plowman, 84, 87
Pliny, 84
Poem by an Operative of Keighley, 163
Poland, 185
Polydore Vergil, 12
Pontefract, 129
Poplins, 120
Portugal, 98, 104
Potter's Field, 94
Power see Horse, Loom, Motive, Steam, Water
Preston, 132, 135
Prices, 11, 56, 65, 81, 94-5, 104, 162, 168, 170
— wool see under Wool
— wool textiles see under Wool Textiles in England

'Privilege', 83
Privy Council, 15, 112
Processes in wool textiles, 118-30
Production
— large-scale, 167
— mass, 151
Protectionist policy
— in England see under Wool Textiles in England
— in other countries see Tariffs

Quills, 75, 90, 118, 125, 133
Quixote, Don, 36

Radcliffe, William, 157
Rambouillet (sheep), 45
Rams, 2, 30, 32-3
Ranches, 5, 42
Range wool, 44
Ranges, public, 4, 5, 44
Rayon, 4, 175
Reed, 142
'Reel-staff', 110
Report on the State of the Woollen Manufacture (1806), 70, 116
Report on the Wool Textile Industry (1947), 148
Restoration (1660), 22, 51, 52, 99
Retailers, 168-9
Revolution (1688), 16, 24, 51, 95, 99, 103, 107, 113-14, 184
Richard I, 11
Ring (spindles), 139, 149, 176
Roberts, Richard, 141
Rochdale, 15, 188
Rock (distaff), 122
Romney Marsh, 22-4
Rope, 133
Roving, 121, 123-4, 136, 137
Roving-frame, 137
Rowers, 75, 88, 118 see also Rowing
Rowing, 54, 130
Russells, 120
Russets, 187
Russia, 4, 37, 108, 185
Russia Company, 95
Rye, 61

Sack, 16 (and note)
Sagathies, 120
Saint Distaff's Day, 84-5
Sandwich, 61, 183
Sanfords, 120
Sarpler, 18-19
Saxony, 30, 37
Says, 56, 61, 181-2
Scarlet cloth, 49, 56, 184

Schofield, 174
Scotland, 34, 58, 84, 89, 117, 127–8,
   145, 192
Scribblers, 154
Scribbling, 90, 127, 153–4, 156
Self-doffer, 149
Serges, 51, 67, 120, 181, 184
Shakespeare, 55, 83, 110
Shalloons, 120, 186–8
Shearing
— cloth see Cloth-finishing
— wool see under Wool
Shearing frame, 158–60
Shearmen, 63, 65–7, 69, 72, 75–6, 78,
   87–8, 113, 118, 159, 160 see also
   Cloth-finishers
Sheep
— branded, 36, 119
— breeds, 2, 32–4 see also Mutton
   breeds
— coat, 1
— Corriedale, 41
— Crossbred see Crossbred
— dual purpose, 34, 38
— emblem of innocence, 185
— English see England
— export of, 33, 36–9, 41–3, 174
— fat-tailed, 43
— fleece, weight of, 4
— Merino see Merino
— mutton sheep see Mutton breeds
— native, 2, 39, 42–3
— number, 3–4, 7
— Rambouillet, 45
— runs, 5, 41 see also station
— size of flocks, 5
— stages in sheep husbandry, 4–5
— trekking, 36–7, 43
— wool sheep, 38
Sheepfarmers, 9–11, 29, 30 see also
   Graziers and under Wool (growers)
Shepherds, 5, 12, 13, 36
Sheppey, 12
Shepton Mallet, 192
Sherborne, 183
Shifts, 151, 170
Shoddy, 4, 173
Short wool see under Wool
Shropshire, 14, 34
Shute, 124
Shuttle, 49, 125–6, 130, 152 see also
   Fly shuttle
Shuttle Club, 132
Silk, 4, 101, 160–1
Silver (mint), 20
Sizing, 91, 127, 157
Skein, 2, 118

Skelton, 188
Skin wool see under Wool
Sley, 125
Slivers, 121, 132, 137, 139, 156
Slubbing, 90, 153, 156
Smiles, 144
Smith, Adam, 25, 29, 54, 70, 97, 116,
   124, 155
Smith, John, 27–9, 120
Smuggling of wool see under Wool
Somerset, Protector, 75
Somersetshire, 15, 158–9, 181, 183–4
Sorts (wool) see under Wool
South Africa (Union of) see Africa
   (South)
Southampton, 61, 67
Southdowns (sheep), 33–4
Spain, 4, 6, 7, 26, 28, 30–2, 36–8, 50,
   61, 98, 184
Specialization, 151, 157, 167–8, 176,
   185, 192
Spindle, 49, 54, 122–4, 134, 137–40,
   148–9, 190
Spindle carriage, 140
Spinners, 9, 63, 67, 69, 72–3, 76, 83–9,
   110, 138–9, 141 see also Spinning
— market, 71, 85
— wages, 86–7, 170
Spinning, 49, 54–5, 75–6, 83–7, 90,
   122–4, 141, 149–50, 153–6, 164, 166,
   169–70 see also Spinners and following
   items
— defects, 85–6, 141
Spinning by rollers, 130, 132–7
Spinning frame see Frame
Spinning Jenny, 138–40, 141, 192
Spinning machines, 86, 141, 149, 155–7,
   167 see also Frame and Spinning by
   rollers
Spinning schools, 86
Spinning wheel, 54, 123–4, 155–6
Spinster, 55, 83, 109, 118
Spole, 133
Spring, Thomas, 76–7
Square Motion, 146
Staffordshire, 191
Staments, 61
Stamford, 56, 61, 179
Standardization of cloth see under Wool
   Textiles in England
Standhill, 138
Staple (fibre), 3, 6, 177
Staple (market) see Wool staple
Staplers see Wool staplers
State control of industry, 54, Chapter 6,
   165–6
Station (sheep), 5, 6, 8, 40

Statute of Apprentices (1563), 82–3, 109, 111, 113, 166
Statutes see Act of Parliament
Steam-power, 137, 156–7
Stock cards, 121
Stock Owners' Association, 37
Stourbridge Fair, 182
Strikes, 116–17, 164–5
Stroud, 129, 183–4
Stroudwater, 76
Stuarts, 17, 111, 181
Stuff, 51, 120, 182, 190
Stuff-damask, 120
Stumpe, William, 76, 78
Style, a clothier, 77
Sudbury, 56, 181
Suffolk, 15, 34, 73, 85, 97, 108, 181–3
Sunday, 129
Surrey, 183
Sussex, 22, 25, 181, 183
Sussex Down (sheep), 34
Sweden, 37, 110
Swift, Jonathan, 74
Sydney, 2
Syracuse Convention, 45, 175

Tame, Edmund, 77
Tame, John, 11, 77
Tammies, 187–8
Tapestry, 61
Tariffs, 16, 30, 44–5, 60, 110, 113, 171–2, 174–5
Taunton, 90, 181, 184
Teasles, 127, 130, 158
Tenter-frame, 54, 105–6, 129, 187
Thierry, Rachel, 67–8
Thoresby, 186
Thorp, 18
Throstle, 137, 141
Thrums, 65
Thursday Market, 93
Tibet, 4
Tiverton, 73, 74, 114, 184
Tom Paine Hall, 94
Tops, 121, 143, 145–6, 167, 173, 176
Top-maker, 167
'Tosed', 64
'To shrink as northern cloths', 185
Touker Street Market, 93
Tow, 84, 122–3
Trade
— cloth see Marketing of cloth
— depressions, 92, 111–4, 171
— free see Free trade
— wool see Marketing of wool
Trade Unionism, 87, 114–17, 160, 163–5

Treadle, 124–6
Treaties, 103–4
Trowbridge, 81
Truck wages, 110, 115
Tuckar, 76
Tudors, 12, 73, 77–8, 103, 111, 166, 181, 188
Turkey, 4, 95–6
Tyndale, 12

Unemployment, 81–2, 92–3, 110–15, 141, 163, 171
United Provinces, 22 see also Low Countries
United States
— customs-houses, 2
— sheep, 4, 5, 37, 43–4, 174
— statistics, 38–9, 43–4
— tariffs, 44–5, 171, 174–5
— wool, 4, 7, 32, 38–9, 43–5, 175
— wool textiles, 30, 150, 166, 172–6
United States Tariff Commission, 1
Uruguay, 4, 39, 42, 172
— statistics, 39, 42

Venetian writers, 12, 32, 51, 181
Venice, 56
Voyages of discovery, 103

Wage-earners, 50, 64, 68–9, 91, 93
Wage system, 80
Wages, 64–5, 73, 76, 78, 81–3, 86–7, 89, 90, 92, 98, 100, 108–10, 112–17, 139–40, 162–6, 170, 176, 190
Wakefield, 67, 94, 180, 186–7
Wales, 15, 34, 58, 66, 181
Walker, 127 see also Fullers
Walloon, 61
Walmersley, 130
Warp, 85, 101, 120, 124–7, 131, 139–40, 142, 155, 157, 184, 190
Warping, 151, 153
Wars, 53, 110, 113, 174, 189
Water-frame, 132, 136–7, 139–40, 156
Water mills, 129
Water-power, 110, 128–9, 137, 141, 156, 191
Waterhouse, Captain, 39
Watts, R., 118–19
Weavers, 56–9, 61–4, 66–73, 76–83, 85–91, 108–10, 113–15, 118–19, 124–6, 130–2, 138, 141, 143, 154–5, 157, 166, 170, 179, 180, 182, 187, 189, 190 see also Weaving
— extinction of hand-loom, 157, 161–4
— several employers, 78, 80–1, 89
— trade unions, 114–15, 163

Weavers, unemployment, 81–2, 141, 163
— wages, 81, 83, 170
Weavers' Act (1555), 77, 80, 166, 181
Weaving, 49, 54, 90, 124–7, 131, 142, 149–54, 157, 166, 170 *see also* Looms *and* Weavers
Weft, 120, 124–6, 131, 139–40, 155, 184
Weights, false, 87
West Country, 70–92, 95, 116, 155, 159, 163, 179, 183–6, 189, 191–2
Westmorland, 85, 158, 181–2, 188
West Riding, 64, 91, 132, 152, 153, 155, 159–60, 163, 182, 185–7, 189, 190 *see also* Yorkshire
White, Sir Thomas, 66
Wholesalers, 168–9
Whorl, 122, 123
Willeying, 90, 120
William III, 52
William of Wykeham, 74
Wiltshire, 78, 88, 111, 130, 155, 159, 183–4
Winchcombe, John, 74, 75, 78, 88, 188
Winchester, 55–6, 58, 179
Winding of yarn, 151, 155
Wines, 104
Witney, 192
Woad, 56
Wolsey, Cardinal, 73, 111
Women, 54–5, 67–8, 75, 81, 83–4, 86, 91–2, 156, 169, 170, 177, 188
Woof, 61, 124
Wool
— African *see* Africa
— American *see* America
— Australian *see under* Australia
— carding *see* Wool-carding
— carpet, 2, 44
— classing, 6, 41 *see also under* Wool (grading)
— clean, 3, 6, 119, 148
— 'clothing', 177
— 'combing', 26, 28, 177, 183
— combing (process) *see* Wool-combing
— cost in cloth and suit, 3
— crossbred *see* Crossbred
— elasticity, 1, 3
— English *see under* England
— exports, 11, 14, 16–32, 56–7, 60–1, 97, 102, 104
— — world, 3–4
— fats, 173
— fineness, 2, 6
— fleece, 6, 105
— French *see under* France

Wool, German, 26, 31, 37 *see also* Saxony
— government purchases, 2
— grades, 2, 3, 14 *see also next item*
— grading, 6, 8 *see also under* Wool (classing)
— grease, 6, 119
— growers, 7–9, 14–19, 27, 29, 69, 120, 175 *see also* Sheep farmers
— handle, 3
— hog's, 6
— lamb's, 6, 105, 119, 185
— long, 2, 3, 6, 15, 33–4, 38, 41, 119, 120, 182–3, 189
— marketing *see* Marketing of wool
— merchants *see* Wool staplers
— merino *see* Merino
— New Zealand *see* New Zealand
— output, world, 3–4
— packing, 6, 18, 54, 67
— prices, 3, 7–9, 16, 18–19, 23, 33
— production, 1–6
— range, 44
— registers, public, 25
— re-worked, 4, 175 *see also* Shoddy
— scouring, 6, 148
— serrations, 1
— shearing, 6, 36
— shoddy *see* Shoddy
— short, 15, 33–4, 38, 119–20, 177
— shrinkage, 6
— skin, 6, 16
— skirting, 6, 41
— smuggling, 22–5, 27–8
— sorting, 67, 75, 118–19, 170, 185 *see also next item*
— sorts, 2, 6, 7, 9, 15, 34, 105, 119
— soundness, 3
— Spanish *see under* Spain
— spinning *see* Spinning
— staple, length of, 3, 6, 177
— supply limited, 6, 39, 43, 155, 161
— territorial, 44
— types, variety of, 1–3
— winding, 119–20
Wool-carders, 67, 73, 88–9, 118, 170 *see also* Wool-carding
Wool-carding, 75–6, 90, 120–1, 153–4, 177 *see also* Wool-carders
— machines, 130, 136–8, 148–9
Wool-combers, 66, 69, 87, 110, 114–16, 121–2, 160–1, 164–5, 170 *see also* Wool-combing
— master, 71, 85
— patron saint, 66, 143
— trade union, 87, 114–16, 164–5
Wool-combers' Association, 165

INDEX

Wool-combing *see also* Wool-combers
— defects, 121–2, 144–5, 165
— machines, 38, 120, 130, 141, 143–50, 160–1, 165, 167, 177
— merits, 146
— operations, 121–2, 154, 166, 170, 177, 182, 190
Wool fats, 173
Wool-fells, 16
Woolmen (merchants), 6, 9, 14, 16–19, 29, 72, 112
Wool merchants *see* Aliens, Woolmen, Wool staplers
Wool packers *see under* Wool (packing)
Woolsack, 10, 51
Wool sorters *see under* Wool (sorting)
Wool staple, 20–1
— merchants of *see* Wool staplers
Wool staplers, 7, 15, 17–21, 79 *see also* Woolmen
Wool Textiles in England
— alien immigrants, 57–62, 183
— cloth, broad *see* Broadcloth
— — compulsory wearing, 98–9
— — definition, 120
— — medley, 130, 159
— — scarlet *see* Scarlet cloth
— — white, 103, 130, 159
— comparison with France, 177
— comparison with United States, 176
— customs duties *see* Tariffs
— dimensions, statutory *see* Assize of Cloth
— early history, 55–62
— employment, 169
— exports, 50–3, 55–6, 60–1, 94–6, 102–6, 108, 110–11, 113, 167, 171–3, 175, 178, 185, 190
— — Empire consumption, 172
— — proportion to total exports, 171
— geographical distribution, Appendix
— imports, 49, 56–7, 60, 104
— integration, 166–7
— inventions, Chapter 7
— manufacturer *see* Manufacturer
— marketing *see* Marketing of cloth
— merchants *see* Merchants
— nineteenth and twentieth centuries, Chapter 8
— number of operatives, 69, 86, 111, 169–70

Wool Textiles in England
— organization, Chapter 5, 166–70
— pre-eminence among English industries, 50-5
— prices, 56, 65, 104
— processes, of manufacture, Chapter 7
— protection, 22, 56–7, 59, 60, 97–105
— social influence, 55
— standardization, 96, 105–8, 166
— state control, 54, Chapter 6, 165–6
— statistics, 60–1, 171–3 *see also above* number of operatives
— structure of industry, 166–9
— unemployment *see* Unemployment
— women *see* Women
Wool textiles in Other Countries, 49–50, 173–8
Worcester, 15, 188, 191
Worcestershire, 181
Working Party Report: Wool (1947), 148
Worstead, 179
Worsteds, 2, 38, 51, 61, 66, 116, 120, 127, 130, 139, 148–50, 152, 156–8, 163–4, 166–71, 176–9, 182, 185–7, 189, 192
— definition of, 120, 127
— worsted carding, 148–9, 177
Worsted Seld, 93
Wyatt, John, 132–4

Yarmouth, 61
Yarn, 14, 55, 105, 121, 139, 141, 150, 152, 156–7, 167, 173, 176–7, 182, 186, 190 *see also* Warp *and* Weft
— count of, 2
— famine, 141
— makers, 14
— stealers, 89
— winding, 151, 155
York, 56, 58, 67, 93, 179–80
Yorkist dynasty, 60
Yorkshire, 15, 69, 71, 78–9, 81, 85, 88, 90–4, 107, 108, 111, 116, 130, 150, 152, 155–6, 158–60, 164, 170, 179–82, 184–7, 189–92 *see also* West Riding
Young, Arthur, 29, 86, 99, 102, 182
Ypres, 11, 16, 50, 67

Zeeland, 58